HARRY OLDFIELD'S INVISIBLE UNIVERSE

Also by Grant Solomon:

Stephen Turoff: Psychic Surgeon

HARRY OLDFIELD'S
INVISIBLE UNIVERSE

The story of one man's search for the healing methods
that will help us survive the 21st century

JANE AND GRANT SOLOMON

Thorsons
An Imprint of HarperCollins*Publishers*

Thorsons
An Imprint of HarperCollins*Publishers*
77–85 Fulham Palace Road
Hammersmith, London W6 8JB

Published by Thorsons 1998

1 3 5 7 9 10 8 6 4 2

A catalogue record for this book
is available from the British Library

ISBN 0 7225 3652 6

Printed in Great Britain by
Creative Print and Design (Wales), Ebbw Vale

For Mum, Dad and Mum

CONTENTS

PREFACE

'Knowing that 23 in binary is 10111 won't help you in a pub fight (in fact, it might even start one...).'
THE OFFICIAL POLITICALLY INCORRECT HANDBOOK

As the above sentiment expresses so succinctly, science is not everybody's first or favourite subject. So in this book we have tried to make *Harry Oldfield's Invisible Universe* as accessible to everyone as possible.

JANE AND GRANT SOLOMON
APRIL 1998

ACKNOWLEDGEMENTS

There have been so many people who have contributed to the making of this book that it is impossible to acknowledge them all personally. So instead we extend our heartfelt thanks to all those who helped in whatever way.

We would like particularly to acknowledge Harry's good friend Peter Williams for his invaluable help and thank Harry's son Anthony for his generosity in sharing his home and his Dad with us for so many hours.

Special thanks go to Eileen Oldfield for her assistance in collating the huge amount of background information pertaining to Harry's work. Without her efforts, this book would not have been possible.

INTRODUCTION

HARRY Oldfield is an inventor, scientist, thinker and somewhat eccentric seeker after new and forgotten knowledge. He is an explorer of undiscovered realms. For Harry, 'not possible' generally translates as 'let's have a look'. For more than two decades, he has been researching his theories about life and its meaning. This research has led him to many incredible discoveries, including that of a 'crystal-dwelling photonic being' – another form of life here with us on Earth.

One of Harry's main developments has been a photo-imaging system that unveils the human aura and indeed many other phenomena. In the autumn of 1995, he was conducting a scientific investigation into the energy configurations surrounding a well-known psychic surgeon, Stephen Turoff. Whilst he was examining the healer's energy field, a face with a beard appeared on his computer screen and smiled at him. This was one of Stephen's spirit guides, a being from another world, another dimension, captured by scientific equipment. From that moment on, Harry became known in some circles as the 'psychic scientist'. He has gone on to image what might be described as 'spirit presences' in mortuaries whilst conducting experiments under the auspices of a coroner and professor of pathology.

But this metaphysical or paranormal aspect of Harry's work is a wholly unintentional by-product of his wide and varied research. One of his most important areas of investigation concerns the use of natural energy as medicine. For some 20 years, Harry has pioneered gentle, non-invasive and inexpensive methods of diagnosis and healing, inventing instruments which are now helping the sick in 20 countries around the world. Those in need of healing also arrive in droves at Harry's clinic in South Ruislip, Middlesex, for consultations with the amazing 'medicine man', as he has been named by his Native American friends.

But Harry is no strange and mysterious mystic. He offers his patients images and measurements, practical solutions and machines to promote healing – truly twenty-first century technology. Doctors and dentists, chemists, vets and other professionals are often astounded by his approach to natural healing. But his methods work.

Who is this modern-day Merlin? He is a generous and big-hearted Londoner whose affable, approachable nature and irrepressible enthusiasm have endeared him to many an initial sceptic. He unreservedly declares that he 'works for God' and his maxim appears to be: 'Give all, help all.' His story is remarkable, his work is undoubtedly controversial and he is now going public with his amazing discoveries.

To share this information simply join us on this journey into the incredible unknown worlds and previously unseen realms of *Harry Oldfield's Invisible Universe*.

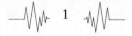

MEETING THE
MEDICINE MAN

Don't bite my finger – look where it's pointing!

WARREN S. McCULLOCH

GRANT'S STORY

I FIRST met Harry Oldfield at his clinic in west London. It was March 1995. For about six years I had been researching the incredible phenomena of psychic surgery and healing, and a few weeks earlier I had met a nurse called Jane Bennett who worked with a biologist who was known, rather intriguingly, as 'the medicine man' by his Native American friends.

During a conversation about our mutual interest in healing Jane had shown me some 'PIPs'. These were amazing coloured images of the human force-field, or 'aura', captured on computer. PIP, Jane informed me, stood for 'polycontrast interference photography'. It was one of Harry Oldfield's inventions. He had apparently also spent the last 20 years developing machines which could both diagnose and treat human energy fields. My curiosity was instantly aroused by the notion that a man of science was exploring the electrical, magnetic and 'subtle' energy fields associated with living humans, the very fields that modern healers, acupuncturists, reflexologists and other 'energy therapists' claimed to be attempting to influence in order to promote 'holistic healing'.

For thousands of years, there have been people able to 'sense' the human energy field, such as the subject of my first book, *Stephen Turoff: Psychic Surgeon* (Thorsons, 1997). In numerous cultures people have been depicted surrounded by haloes of light. Eastern medicine has long relied on pictures and charts of the aura, with its energy centres, or 'chakras' (the Sanskrit word for 'wheel'), and energy flow lines, or 'meridians'. Similar ideas were part of folk medicine in the West, too, until biochemical techniques started to gain prominence a couple of centuries ago.

I knew that medical doctors had scoffed at the idea of micro-organisms as a cause of death before the invention of the microscope revealed the micro-universe. Now I was excited by the possibility that scientific instruments might reveal the chakras, meridians and energy fields of the 'energy-universe'.

We are not only considering here the generally accepted energy-universe on what we might call the physical or material plane. Rather, the proposition is that other energy-universes may exist on what are often called 'related planes of reality'. A commonly offered explanation is that these planes are 'other dimensions where matter is vibrating at higher frequencies than matter in the physical plane'.

Take as an analogy different octaves of musical notes. One scale would represent the plane of our physical universe where our matter and energy are interchangeable. The next scale would be in a harmonically related but quite different higher octave, a different plane. These different octaves or planes could actually occupy the same space and yet be 'separate realities'.

To take this point further, another analogy often used is the 'ghosting' effect that sometimes happens when we watch TV. We may be on a particular channel, but, due to signal interference, the broadcast from a second channel may also be visible on screen. In effect, there are two broadcasts, representing two different 'realities', occupying the same space.

To me, the fact that a scientist might have found a way of picking up a second channel and superimposing it on our normal one – by design – was certainly a top priority well worth investigating.

I picked Jane up as arranged and we drove to the Clinic and School of Electro-Crystal Therapy in South Ruislip, west London.

We drew up outside the medium-sized suburban semi-detached house, having arrived in good time, and Jane settled me in with a cup of tea and a biscuit. Friendly place, I remember thinking. As if to confirm my first impression, Harry emerged from the kitchen, beaming from ear to ear, with a mug of steaming tea cupped between both hands. He was a large, bouncy, jovial man, standing about six feet tall in his sandals.

'Good morning, Mr Solomon,' he said rather formally and then turned away as if distracted by some important thought or other.

I knew the intention was for computerized video pictures to be taken of my energy field but beyond that I had no idea what to expect. Jane then informed Harry that we had discussed the possibility of capturing healing energies on the PIP system.

I had learned from my six years of studying healing that we are all capable of doing hands-on healing to some degree. It's a natural skill, like singing. However, I had also learned that, as with singing, some of us just 'croak' in the bath whilst others become Pavarottis. The idea of capturing these normally invisible healing energies on film was fascinating and I could hardly wait for the PIP scanning session to begin.

Harry suggested I might like to 'warm up'. Jane sat on a chair in the waiting room whilst I performed healing for a few minutes on her head and shoulders. Soon the warmth which is often associated with healing energy was apparent to both of us and we concluded that everything was flowing and that it was time to take some pictures.

We went into Harry's 'laboratory', a small room off the kitchen. This small room, which doubles as his consulting room, was filled to the ceiling with microscopes, cameras, crystals, books, papers, plants, graphs, a few personal items and, of course, the computerized video scanning system known as PIP. Harry explained it in simple terms (which was just as well!):

'Some individuals, "sensitives", say they can see the energy fields around people. The subtle aspects of this electromagnetic field effect are sometimes referred to as the "aura". Diagrams of it can be found in many cultures. Ancient Hindu books called the *Upanishads*, for example, contain detailed pictures of the various energy centres or zones. I don't need to go into details, but I can tell you that the different numbers of petals they allocated to the flowers which were used to depict the seven main chakra centres or energy configuration points give a very accurate indication of the harmonic frequencies – what we might call "rates of vibration" – of these energy centres.

'I've been trying for many years to find ways to unveil these previously invisible phenomena with my instruments.'

Given that Harry needed a highly sophisticated modern instrument to view the energy field, I immediately wondered how ancient people ascertained this information. Much later, having been pointed in the right direction by Harry, I learned that the *Upanishads* are over 5,000 years old, so it is unlikely that these people were 'measuring' the phenomenon with scientific instruments. One possibility is that some of their number could 'see' what was then recorded.

In the case of the meridians, said to be the channels of life energy, or *chi*, which flows around the body, we can look to the ancient Chinese. They described the meridians' hundreds of minor junctions, or acupuncture points, in the first writings on acupuncture, the *Nei Jing*, which appeared thousands of years ago. These writings contain many of today's principles of Traditional Chinese Medicine.

Harry continued his explanation:

'Sensitives describe the aura as a corona of different coloured lights which flicker and flow around the body. Most people cannot see it, though, so what we've developed here is a system which uses an artificial eye, the video camera, with an artificial brain, the micro-chip computer. The electrical wire from one to the other represents the artificial optic nerve.

'Whilst the signal information gained by sensitives is very useful to them as individuals, the advantage of the PIP system from a scientific standpoint is that its representation of the energy field is always the same no matter who uses it, whereas the descriptions of auras given by different sensitives vary markedly so it is difficult to make objective comparisons.

'To accept that people can see and interpret these signals is no harder to accept than that some people are long sighted and some are short sighted. In the same way, some species, like dogs, are adapted to pick up certain signals and other species, like bats, pick up other signals. We all have different natural capabilities to help us experience life. Nature does not produce clones!

'The PIP instrumentation employs a device which can distinguish between many different grades or qualities of light. The innovation is in the computer programme, which allocates a number to each grade of light and then colour codes each number. The end result is the image you see on the computer screen.

'The colours and patterns making up this image will tell me a great deal about you.'

I learned from Harry that for the best PIP results the subject needs to undress to their underwear so that the equipment can register reflections from the body surface without interference from clothes. I duly undressed to my boxer shorts. Harry asked me to stand in front of a large white roller-blind which, when extended, covered one wall of his laboratory. He explained that this was to provide a monochromatic background against which my energy field would be clearly highlighted. He then took up the video camera in his left hand and double-clicked the computer mouse with his right to initiate the computer programme.

'Could you point your hand at the floor and imagine you're still healing?'

I did as requested and watched the computer screen, which showed a close-up of my hand as Harry zoomed in with the video camera.

'Look at the screen,' Harry exclaimed suddenly. 'Do you see the strands of blue-green energy coming from your hand? That's the healing energy. And look, there are strands being drawn from the ground as well. It looks as though they're matching the strands from each of the fingers.'

Harry quickly clicked the computer mouse to grab the frame and the image was captured.

A few seconds later the strands coming from my hands met up with those emanating from the ground and Harry grabbed another image. He attempted an explanation: 'Perhaps an analogy in nature would be lightning, which works in much the same way – electrical energy is drawn up from the ground to meet the energy descending from the sky. Normally, of course, most people wouldn't be able to see what just happened, but with PIP everyone can see it.'

Needless to say, I was very excited by this demonstration.

Then Harry scanned my energy field and captured and saved a number of images on file, which he then analysed. The first piece of information was very accurate.

'Your liver,' Harry began, pointing to a pattern of dark red patches, which he called 'clouds', in the region of my lower right ribs, 'appears to be dealing with a large amount of toxins at the moment. Have you had a lot of alcohol in the last 24 hours?'

Guilty as charged! A business lunch the day before had got a bit out of hand and we had ended up with an early evening session in the pub before going on to a night-club. Good for business, it turned out, but perhaps not so good for my liver?

Harry was meanwhile scrutinizing the image of the space between my legs.

'Hmmm,' he mused, staring at the concentric rings of energy flow, 'there's quite a lot of turbulence and depletion in your base area.'

He again had my full and undivided attention – but this turned out to be less serious than it sounded. It simply meant that there was probably a lot of important change going on in my life. Since at that time I was switching career and moving house, I considered this to be somewhat better than a good guess on Harry's part. On top of this, he explained that the 'depletion' could probably be put down to my lifestyle and habits making me more than a little tired. Harry was, however, scrupulously careful to make observations rather than judgements. Strangely, for me, his reserve had the effect of highlighting the problem areas and emphasizing that a degree of change was called for.

Next, Harry told me that I had a sore throat. The thick red circle under my chin was very pronounced on the screen. 'You also had a back injury, in the region of the coccyx, many years ago,' he commented.

Aged 10, I had fallen backwards off a shed, landed on an upturned wheelbarrow and injured the base of my spine. I had to ask, 'How on earth did you know that?'

He replied:

'There is an "echo" in your energy field. The PIP system gives information about imbalances in your energy field. This field is like an electronic *Doppelgänger*, or double, a template onto which your physical molecules are strung. When the field is out of balance, the physical cells will follow, and vice versa.

'As we have just seen by looking at your back, the system is able to detect echoes from past trauma or illness.

'Sometimes we see a persistent or continuing area of energy imbalance and then find that the person goes on to develop a related physical problem.'

Harry printed off the saved colour images of my energy field. He explained that after diagnosis, the next logical step was 'treatment using an energy input to balance your energy field'.

Harry called Jane in and she put a clear plastic-looking tube containing various tiny coloured crystal chips in saline solution around my neck and rested another, coiled, on my liver, with some support from my clothes. The tubes were attached, via electrical wires, to a box the size of a toaster. On the front panel of the box were three dials. Jane set these to the 'balancing frequency for the throat and solar plexus chakras'. The throat chakra setting was obviously to do with my sore throat. The solar plexus chakra, I was informed, 'governs the liver in electro-crystal therapy'.

For the remaining 20 minutes of my consultation I sat comfortably, sipping contentedly at my second cup of tea, and within ten minutes my sore throat had gone! Unfortunately, I had another lunch appointment to go to immediately afterwards, so whatever benefit the treatment may have achieved for my liver was probably negated instantly!

I would soon learn that I was not the only person to be impressed with Harry's innovations, especially the electro-crystal therapy treatment. A little while later I travelled to the School of Electro-Crystal Therapy to talk to Harry about this book and met Detective Superintendent Jock Fraser (retired) of the Metropolitan Police.

Jock Fraser is approaching 70, but clearly was once a very powerful man. He has what we might describe as a gruff exterior but this hides a good-humoured and gentle nature. In his younger days he wrestled, ran and swam. He also played football, hockey and rugby, as a prop-forward, for the police.

'There were a few what we might call "physical encounters" in my work too,' he confided with a wink. 'All this added up to a body which had taken a bit of a bashing and by the time I retired the knees and back were especially troublesome.'

Jock lived just down the road from Harry and he used to stop and have a chat with Michael Fitzpatrick, who ran the local antique jeweller's shop and made Harry's electro-crystal accessories to order.

'Michael is Irish and I'm Scottish,' he told me, 'so you could say we regularly exchanged a bit of good-natured Celtic banter.'

But one morning when he passed by the shop, Jock was not his usual jolly self.

'What's the matter with you today?' enquired Michael.

'Well, just look at my hands,' was the reply.

Jock lifted his arms and stretched out his fingers, and Michael saw that his friend's hands were twice their normal size.

'One of my boys had to come round to dress me this morning,' continued Jock.

'I've got just the job for you,' said Michael and motioned for Jock to follow him inside the shop. He handed the big man a small green nugget the size of a hazelnut. 'Hold that and sit down. I'll make a cup of tea.'

The Scotsman sat in a chair with the little green lump cupped between his swollen hands while the Irishman went off to make the tea. Just 15 minutes later, Jock was amazed to find he could pick up his cup with no problem. His hands had miraculously shrunk to their normal size.

'What is that green stuff?'

'It's a healing crystal called green peridot,' said Michael and promptly put the gem in his pocket. Jock was so impressed that he listened intently to Michael's explanation about how crystals had been used for centuries for their natural healing properties. 'And there's an inventor chappy down the road who gets me to make up crystal attachments for his machines so that energy can be pulsed through the crystals and the healing effect is increased tenfold!'

'That introduction to the healing power of crystals was five or six years ago,' Jock told me. He later went to see Harry and began using electro-crystal therapy. Once, after climbing too many steps on a Jack the Ripper tour of London, 'My legs filled my trousers to bursting. A couple of treatments with Harry's crystal machine and I was fine. I was so keen to find out how it all works that I recently enrolled on a course and bought my own electro-crystal generator. Wonderful little gadget it is.'

Stories such as these and my experiences that first morning at the Clinic and School of Electro-Crystal Therapy had a profound effect on me.

I had first come across energy fields in my research into the life and work of Stephen Turoff. Stephen had told me about the colours and patterns he sees around people all the time. Like many others who see or sense it, he called this system of colours and patterns the 'aura'. Now Harry seemed to have invented a machine that could show up the aura for *everybody* to see. Not only this, but he also appeared to be able to photographically capture the healing energy coming from a person who was merely imagining doing healing, as well as to glean a great deal of useful clinical information from a brief assessment of the coloured patterns produced and recorded by his PIP scanner. And anyone, he claimed, could be trained to 'read' these energy field pictures.

In addition, the fact that Harry seemed to have developed a scientific instrument which used the energy field for healing in the same way that healers and natural energy therapists claimed to do, opened up exciting possibilities for the future. It meant that people without access to a healer could treat their own energy field by learning a series of settings on a panel of dials. Harry's portable machine could be used at home, work or even in the car or on a train.

The potential for this work seemed endless.

JANE'S STORY

My story begins five years earlier, in the summer of 1990.

A late shift at the local hospital. Nursing handover.

'You take rooms 24 to 29, Jane. That gives you three patients for operation, two first day post-operation and one lady with terminal cancer who is in for investigations. Do you think you can manage that?'

'Yes, I should be fine.'

The sister and I discussed the care of the patients assigned to me. As usual it promised to be busy. Weekdays were full of scheduled operations and I would have to make frequent trips to and from the operating theatre.

First things first. I decided to check on Mrs Weston in room 24. I had been told she had terminal bowel cancer but was doing very well. She was outliving her prognosis and her pain was well controlled with very little medication. I went into her room.

'Hello, Mrs Weston. I'm Jane. I'll be looking after you this afternoon. Can I do anything for you?'

'Hello, Jane. I'm a little cold, do you think you could get me another blanket please? And do call me June.'

Another blanket was duly fetched. On rearranging the covers I noticed a small white machine under the blankets.

'What's that, a TENS machine?' I asked. TENS machines were the latest scientific invention, introduced to help pain by means of a mild electric current generally, though not always, applied to the skin in the area of discomfort.

'No, it's an electro-crystal therapy machine,' June replied. She lifted up her nightie to reveal a small glass tube, seemingly full of small coloured stones, resting on her lower abdomen. This tube was attached, by a wire, to the small white machine. June handed me the tube to look at. As I took the crystal-filled tube I felt a soothing, calming feeling. How strange, I remember thinking, must be my imagination.

'What does it do?'

'It balances my energy field,' replied June matter of factly. I was none the wiser, but having little time to chat, promised June that I would be back soon to check she was comfortable.

I had no time to think about what had happened as I was busy with the routine of post-operative care, regulating drips, checking blood pressure and giving out pain-killers. In fact, the whole incident might well have slipped my mind had June and her husband, Robert, not been so determined to tell me about electro-crystal therapy. The next time I went into June's room, Robert handed me a small leaflet on the School of Electro-Crystal Therapy. I promised I would read it.

June continued her story. 'I treat myself daily as it helps keep the pain under control and I'm able to boost the energy to my immune system, which helps me fight the cancer. I also give myself a general energy boost if I'm feeling a little tired. I see an electro-crystal therapist from time to time who assesses my energy field and advises me on which frequencies to use.'

'How do you change the frequency?' I asked.

She showed me the frequency control knobs on the front of the machine. Robert promised that the next day he would bring in the book written by the inventor of the machine.

That night as I was travelling home, I wondered how a machine could do so much. Was it just the placebo effect? Using devices for pain relief was not difficult to understand, as such machines were already in use, but a machine which could give you energy? And boost your immune system? It sounded too good to be true.

My mother always says that her daughter does not like to miss out on anything (her polite way of saying I am nosey), so, true to form, I decided to investigate. I started to read the book Robert brought in, *The Dark Side of the Brain* (Harry Oldfield and Roger Coghill, Element Books, 1988). What I found interesting were the case histories written by people, some of them seriously ill, who had been helped by electro-crystal therapy. If there really were machines that could help people heal in a non-invasive way then this was an opportunity not to be missed. I had to know more. A couple of months later saw me arriving at the School of Electro-Crystal Therapy armed with pen, notepaper and a healthy scepticism. Harry Oldfield would be teaching the weekend course and I hoped that it would be just as interesting as his book. I was, however, totally unprepared for the radical change in thought which would result from what I was about to learn.

My fellow students were a mixed bunch. They included a carpenter, a musician, an osteopath, a housewife, an electrical engineer and a medical doctor. We sat in a semi-circle and introduced ourselves. We all had our reasons for being there. Some had come out of curiosity, having heard of positive responses from people who had been treated by electro-crystal therapy. The professional carers wanted to incorporate the therapy into their existing practice. The housewife wanted to help her sick husband who had been discharged from hospital, the doctors unable to do any more for him.

Harry Oldfield was very much younger than I had imagined. He was (and still is) very down to earth, with a well developed sense of humour and he seemed genuinely concerned for the welfare of his patients and fellow human beings. We discussed energy fields. I was amazed how imbalances in the energy field could be detected with a small hand-held scanner. Harry called this method the electro-scanning method, or ESM. We were shown how to do this.

One fellow student, George, had rather bad hayfever. His eyes were streaming and his nose and sinuses blocked. I was volunteered, by Harry, to scan him in front of the whole group. I got up apprehensively, inwardly reminding myself of the scanning procedure and hoping that I would not make too much of a hash of it. (Some of you electro-crystal therapists out there, whom I have helped to train over the last few years, may find this scenario amusing.) The scan revealed George's energetic imbalances. High readings were measured over his eyes, sinuses and immune system (which is typical in allergies). These imbalances were then to be corrected using electro-crystal therapy. It was simply a matter of playing the correct frequency back to the area concerned.

Sounded simple enough, but would it work? Another student was instructed by Harry to set up treatment. One flexible tube, containing crystals and saline, was placed around George's forehead 'to treat the energy of the eyes and sinuses', while another was placed over the breast bone 'to treat the energy of the immune system'. Both were attached to electro-crystal generators set on calming frequencies. George sat happily, looking a little like Hiawatha (without the feather) as the course continued. Twenty minutes later, Harry asked him how he was feeling. Hiawatha beamed.

'It's incredible! I can breathe through my nose for the first time in weeks and my eyes feel cool, as though there's a breeze on them.'

I was impressed, but still a little sceptical. Could it be mind over matter?

During the weekend a fair number of patients came to tell us of their experiences with electro-crystal therapy. The stories they told did not fit in with my nursing experience and I wondered if they could have been imagining things. However, they seemed to be normal, everyday folk. One thing that could not possibly be misinterpreted was the fondness which existed between them and Harry. Some of them were nervous at having to tell their tales in front of 15 strangers, but if they faltered, or stumbled over their words, Harry was there with them, giving them a word of encouragement, or empathy, or yet another joke to help them relax.

One patient sticks in my mind. He told us how a year or so earlier he had been diagnosed with a brain tumour. He had had conventional treatment but remained very ill. This gentle man had heard of Harry Oldfield and, deciding that he had nothing to lose, had thought he would give the therapy a try.

Two friends had practically carried him in on his first visit. His eyesight was deteriorating rapidly and he was virtually paralysed on one side of his body. He told us how Harry had calmed the energy to the head over the area of the tumour and the energy to the immune system had been boosted to help the body fight the cancer cells. His general field had been treated with 'balancing frequencies'. After his first session he had walked out with much less support than he had needed on the way in. Now he reported he was feeling much better. The doctors were baffled by the dramatic improvement in his eyesight!

My first course weekend over, I made the decision to buy an electro-crystal generator. I had to give this thing a fair crack of the whip. 'Seeing is believing' they say and I was looking forward to seeing for myself just what this machine could do.

Luckily, my family tolerated my frequent requests to scan them. No sooner were they through the door than I had whipped out the scanner and had them taking off their jewellery and watches (metal interferes with the scan). Initially, the most interesting complaint was a swollen, itchy mosquito bite which I treated after looking in the manual for the correct treatment setting. Yes, true; it did improve and the next day was a lot smaller and less irritating, but then mosquito bites do tend to do that anyway. Then, after about a month of treating Dad's blocked sinuses, which did improve (could it have been because he finally cut down on cigars?), and an elderly fatigued cat, which did perk up (could it have been not so many nights on the tiles?), something extraordinary happened.

I planned to visit my friend Gloria one evening for the usual 50 cups of tea and chat. I had my trusty electro-crystal therapy machine with me. I'd taken to carrying it around just in case something dramatic happened. Gloria answered the door looking very much the worse for wear, an eye pad on one eye and a pained expression in the other.

'Oh Jane, it's you! Thank God. I've been waiting for you to come to take me to the hospital. I'm in agony!' Gingerly, she started to put on her coat, making sure she kept her head as still as possible.

'What on earth's happened to your eye?'

'I was doing keep fit this morning and I poked my finger in my eye. The fingernail went right up under my eyelid. It was really painful and swollen so I went to the hospital. The doctor told me that it was a severe abrasion under the lid. They put this eye pad on, told me to take painkillers and go back tomorrow morning for another check-up. I've had painkillers, but they haven't worked. I'm in so much pain that I don't know what to do. Could you take me back to the hospital?'

My immediate reaction on seeing my friend so distressed was to agree. Then I remembered my electro-crystal generator. Perhaps it would be able to help? I suggested to Gloria that it was probably inflammation causing the pain. I was confident that there was no foreign body involved as the eye would have been well inspected at the hospital earlier in the day. I tentatively suggested to her that we try electro-crystal therapy for 20 minutes and if there were no improvement then I would take her to the hospital.

'Okay, Jane, I'll try anything to get rid of this pain. Just tell me what to do,' she said wearily.

'Sit down and I'll give you a tube to hold next to your eye. We'd better leave the eye pad on to protect it.'

I connected the tube to the machine and set it to what I hoped, from memory, was an anti-pain/anti-inflammatory setting. Unfortunately, I hadn't got my manual with me – just when I needed it most.

We sat quietly, Gloria holding the crystal and saline tube adjacent to her injured eye. She refused my offer to make her a cuppa.

She must be ill.

Twenty minutes went by. Harry had said on the course that this is a good average treatment time. I stood up and reached for the tube, half expecting Gloria to say she was ready to go to the hospital. She moved the tube out of my reach.

'Get out of it! You're not having it, I'm enjoying it too much. It's sending lovely warm pulsations over my eye and the pain's not so bad.'

I was truly astonished. This thing really worked!

'Put the kettle on, Jane. I'm gasping.'

She must be better.

For the next couple of hours we sat and chatted (and drank tea), Gloria giving me a running commentary on the sensations she was getting around her injured eye as the treatment continued. I was not concerned at the length of the treatment time as Harry had said that longer treatments were often administered according to need. Gloria mostly described a soothing warmth and a gradual lessening of the pain. I was curious to see what was happening to the eye under the pad. Unfortunately we had nothing with which to secure it back in place, so we had to leave well alone.

After about two hours Gloria excitedly exclaimed, 'I can open my eye! I can feel a thick tear coming out of the corner.'

Oh, for a piece of sticking plaster or Sellotape to stick that eye pad on again! I was dying to have a look.

'I think that's enough treatment for now, Jane. My eye doesn't hurt at all.'

Gloria went back to the hospital the next day and saw the same doctor, who examined the eye and was astonished. 'Sister, look at this eye. I don't believe it. It's healed!'

Gloria and I had anticipated this response, and Gloria was ready with a small information leaflet on electro-crystal therapy. The doctor promised to read it.

I visited Gloria the next day to see her eye for myself. It looked normal: no swelling, no redness. Gloria no longer had to wear the eye pad and she reported that there had been no further pain since the treatment. She was delighted.

So now I had my proof. I had certainly never heard of a placebo effect of such magnitude. Mind over matter was also ruled out as Gloria knew next to nothing about the therapy and how it worked, let alone had any faith in it. Indeed, she told me after-wards that she had tried it out of desperation, not confidence.

I continued nursing as usual, as it was what I knew best, but gradually, over the next couple of years, I found myself question-ing more and more the wisdom of some of the invasive proce-dures involved in orthodox medical care. Was it always necessary to cut things out? I found myself feeling uneasy as I dished out the tablets on the drug round. What about the side-effects? Surely all of this was just treating symptoms and not getting to the root of the problem?

I chatted to a few doctors, telling them of my new experiences with electro-crystal therapy. Some were genuinely interested, others merely polite. Somehow my offers of demonstrations or talk of clinical trials being set up all came to nothing. Most doctors were, of course, already heavily committed in their own spheres. I became increasingly frustrated, first with the invasive-ness of many of the procedures of orthodox medicine and second with the fact that people did not realize that there might be other approaches to the healing of their disease.

Basically I was no longer sure I was in the right job. Soon after, I was to find myself working with Harry at his clinic and then, later, teaching electro-crystal therapy to others.

HARRY OLDFIELD'S
INVISIBLE UNIVERSE

'I am very interested in the Universe – I am specializing in the
Universe and all that surrounds it.'

PETER COOK

F ROM our research it appears that little Harold Oldfield
would like to have been born with 10,000 fingers. Then he
could have had one in every sticky pie that has ever been
placed before him!

Insatiably inquisitive, the scope of this ostensibly ordinary man's
horizons appears to be infinite. Aged just 12, his fertile mind
devised a food production process which had thus far eluded industry and he sold it to a fish-food company which still makes
profits from it today. Nicknamed 'The Mad Professor' early in
his career – for an explosion that demolished a laboratory – this
affable, eccentric inventor is a British boffin in every sense of
the term. He is perhaps best summed up as the latest in a tradition of 'string and sealing wax' inventors.

In his early twenties, Harry became internationally known in
certain medical circles as the 'darling' of diagnosis – with his
Kirlian gun. This instrument, a sort of biological sonar device,
beamed harmless energy signals into people and listened to
the response in order to diagnose disease. It was a medical first
in that it seemed to be able to accurately detect force-fields of
energy around people and things and obtain pertinent diagnostic

information in the process. Harry originally got the idea whilst watching Dr McCoy scanning a crew member in *Star Trek*'s sick-bay.

Such was the medical interest in his devices that Harry was persuaded to work on the diagnosis of cancer and other diseases with some London hospitals.

Then Harry crossed a line he did not know existed. He started to notice that some conventional treatments were distorting people's energy fields and set about inventing machines which could treat the fields to overcome this. The hospitals distanced themselves immediately and Harry was left high and dry. But he picked himself up, dusted himself down and began his search for the meaning of life in earnest ... well, in his garden shed actually.

That was 20 or so years ago. Since then, Harry has been journeying through the strange new worlds of the invisible universe, researching his theories about life and its meaning. His field of investigation is wide and nothing is considered impossible or irrelevant.

This approach has led to some remarkable developments, including an environmentally-friendly plastic-eating bug. Harry says: 'The plan is for us to have aesthetically pleasing "disposal lakes" in which these benevolent little creatures would live and eat anything plastic that was thrown to them.' A rather interesting and unintended aspect of this work is that these hungry little monsters have a waste product which Harry uses as fertilizer in his garden!

Then there is the portable smoke mask. Some years ago Harry saw television pictures of Chinese children who had died in a cinema fire. Such was his concern that he immediately developed an easy to produce and highly portable emergency smoke mask.

These inventions and discoveries are considered by many to be interesting and significant. But Harry considers one of his discoveries to be by far the most important of all: that of the crystal-dwelling photonic being. This is a (probably) silicon-based life(?) presence which appears to make its home in crystals.

The story of its discovery is told by Helen Knowles, one of Harry's co-researchers on the ground-breaking 'crystal entity' project:

'SNOOPY', THE CRYSTAL ENTITY LIFE-FORM

'It began at a mind, body and spirit exhibition, when I saw an aqua-aura crystal and kept going back to look at it. It was more expensive than usual, because aqua-aura is coated with gold wash. I did not altogether know if that was a good idea, but when I held it, it vibrated very strongly. Lunch went out the window and I bought it.

'Some months later, I was attending an advanced [electro-crystal therapy] course and Harry asked us all to bring our own video cassette and any crystals we wanted scanned by PIP the following day. I did not want to miss such an opportunity and brought a huge biscuit tin-ful along, plus a load of rings. I had noticed that my huge rough amethyst quartz ring, which I had worn for over a decade, had sadly lost nearly all its colour and presumably much energy. I was interested to see how it might look on PIP compared with some of the rings and other crystals in my possession, which felt vibrationally active at the time.

'Decked in an old blue bikini I had always worn for PIP purposes, I stood in front of the screen whilst Harry did a quick scan to see how I was bearing up. We then started to go through my hoard of rings and crystals. We saw that the amethyst ring appeared to have lost all its energy but that some of the other rings were very active, as were many of the crystals. As Harry continued with the PIP scan, I picked up my favourite aqua-aura crystal.

'Suddenly I was looking at the VDU screen transfixed. Harry shouted, "Don't move, Helen. This is an historic moment – this is a phenomenon." I was petrified. "It looks like a slug," he said. "Look at it crawling around the crystal!"

' "Oh my God, oh my God," I uttered, too petrified to move. It was all very well Harry saying don't move, but how could we know what it was? I held my body still but my brain said, "Please don't let this thing come into my body, God, I don't know what it is. I'm so scared."

'Perhaps realizing my quandary, Harry suddenly exclaimed, "It's okay, it's white, it's okay. Just don't move, Helen, whatever you do. We must capture this for posterity."

'After the initial shock, I stopped being afraid in a few seconds flat, because the fascination was greater than any fear. This thing had its own aura and was moving and undulating about the crystal. We watched the screen in silence, spellbound.

'Then Harry said, "Look, it's moving around again."

'At those words, it suddenly appeared to dive back into the crystal cluster and the computer crashed. Again Harry said, "Don't move, whatever you do." He started the computer up again. And there was "Snoopy" coming back out.

'This computer failure happened a couple more times. It was as if Snoopy didn't want us to see him, as if he'd been caught out. Perhaps he had.

'Harry thought for a bit and said, "Maybe there are some things we're not supposed to see."

'But we had seen it and what's more it could not be refuted because it was captured on video.'

Other researchers have since conducted their own independent investigations and seen the same phenomenon. One such is Hilmar Orn Hilmarson, an Icelandic colleague of Harry's. Hilmar has been aware of crystal entities for some time. He reports that he can even sense them tickling the hairs on his arm when they venture out of a crystal he is holding. Once a PIP video was made of this as it happened.

Harry asks:

'So what are we to make of this phenomenon apparently made visible by PIP technology?

'For centuries people have reported seeing movements and emanations in and around stones and crystals. Folklore is full of dragons in caves, leprechauns dancing on rocks, fairies at the bottom of the garden and so on. In ancient literature, especially that of the East, the notion of undulating, non-physical shape-changers is commonplace. Are all these reported sightings explainable? Or is there a phenomenon "out there" – or "in there" – which most of us just haven't been able to see thus far?'

Could it be that Harry has found a way to see these beings from folklore? As he says,

'Some scientists believe they have recently discovered evidence of life on Mars. That's interesting and important. But I believe we have very good evidence of another form of life living right here with us, right now.

'We have been studying these beings with the PIP imaging system for some time now. I believe that further research needs to be done in their natural habitat, the crystal mines of the world. We need to find answers to questions like: How were they created? What is their life-cycle? Are they intelligent? Can we communicate with them?

'I think that they may be an endangered species due to intensive mining activity in their natural environment. They appear to need no water and could exist in conditions far more hostile than we humans could bear. This means they could pre-date us by millions of years.'

The implications of this work are far-reaching. We search the universe looking for planets which could support 'intelligent life'. But what we usually mean by this is life like our own which needs water and breathes oxygen. What if other forms of life, aliens as we describe them, are invisible to our senses? What if they do not need water or oxygen? What if they can exist in extremes of temperature that would be intolerable to us? And, most importantly, what if some of these life-forms are not aliens at all, but were here on Earth before us and are still here with us now? What if?

Given that it was a machine, PIP, that allowed this phenomenon to be made visible, we became very interested in the other potential applications of Harry's theories and technology.

PIP has a number of potential applications and there will almost certainly be more in the future as the technology is refined. As to the current uses, one of the main applications is in the medical field. At present there is interest from complementary practitioners but more conventional medical applications may arise in the future. Although for centuries, energy or vibrational medicine treatments, therapies and techniques such as acupuncture, reflexology, homoeopathy and so on have been practised effectively, it has only been in the last few years that any serious credibility has been given to the study of such medicine. The main problem seems to have been the lack of machines and instruments which could make information available to the human senses (especially the optical sense) in an understandable form – we do seem to prefer to see it before we allow ourselves to believe it.

An example of this is the 'heat' generated during hands-on healing. The patient senses (i.e. feels) this and the practitioner knows that a phenomenon akin to heat is being generated under his or her hands. But since a thermometer would not confirm either person's experience, the phenomenon 'does not exist' for orthodox science and the testimony of the people involved is ignored. Harry believes that in such healing people may be experiencing an 'energy transfer' via the healer/patient contact and that the brain interprets the sensation as heat in order to make some physical sense of it. This is the nearest the brain can get to interpreting the phenomenon.

The search for machines and instruments with which to measure such phenomena is going on in many countries at the moment and Harry Oldfield appears to be making a major contribution. Both PIP and his other main diagnostic technique, ESM, can be used to measure both the quality and quantity of the various aspects of the energy field respectively.

ESM was invented first. It gives *quantitative* measurements of the energy field using sound and radio frequencies which are beamed into the subject and recorded as they emerge from the body. If the returning signals are normal, then there is no problem. If they are abnormal, a treatment is recommended.

PIP gives semi-*qualitative* analysis using a video camera and computer to measure light reflected by the subject's energy field. Light enters the energy field from the environment, interacts with the field on a very subtle level and bounces off into the environment again. PIP is designed to get diagnostic information from this ambient light and human energy field interaction.

Some scientists have been more interested in ESM than PIP because they prefer to work with numerical values. Others have questioned whether the two methods are in fact measuring the same phenomenon. But since they do indeed appear to work, are cheap, easy to learn and easy to use for both the therapist and the patient – with no repeat costs like prescribed and over-the-counter drugs – Harry's therapies and techniques do seem ideally placed to spread around the world. It is true that the equipment currently needs mains electricity or batteries, but even this will be done away with when the clockwork versions become available.

In order to understand PIP better we decided to arrange demonstrations of it for audiences throughout Britain and get feedback from the general public. Then, having spent a year demonstrating PIP at exhibitions around the country nearly every weekend and getting some very favourable feedback, we felt confident enough to begin experimental research in conjunction with the psychic surgeon Stephen Turoff at his Danbury Healing Clinic, which is held at the Miami Hotel, Chelmsford, Essex. It was decided that we should create the same conditions as at Harry's clinic and set up a four-foot white light source on the ceiling of one of the therapy rooms. We began using the PIP equipment on one Saturday each month. When Stephen first saw the PIP screen, he was intrigued. 'That's like a cartoon version of what I see with my eyes,' he told us. For the last 25 years he has used this natural ability as an aid in his healing practice.

Up to 40 people now visit for each of the PIP sessions at the Danbury Healing Clinic and this has created a great deal of interest.

Harry feels that PIP is only limited at the moment by the available technology. He believes that as computer and video technology improves and comes closer to the information recognition capability of the eye/brain mechanism, PIP will be able to show us far more – perhaps even the invisible universe of 'spirit beings'.

Stephen's spirit guide Dr Kahn may in fact already have been seen on the PIP screen. Grant recounted how this happened in his book about the psychic surgeon:

'Early in 1995 we invited Stephen to meet Harry for research purposes and an exchange of ideas. Present at the research session were myself, Jane, Harry Oldfield and Len Randall, a man with an interest in all things metaphysical and paranormal...

'In Harry's PIP studio, where he has set up his energy field photography equipment, Stephen stood against the white background which hangs from the ceiling to the floor. Harry manned the video camera and asked me to be in charge of the computer mouse. Jane and Len were to watch Stephen and the computer screen for anything unusual.

'Stephen put his head back slightly and began concentrating, putting himself in what he calls "healing mode". After very few seconds, a circle of yellow light appeared above his head on the computer screen. It changed colour to pink and then white.

' "We may be witnessing a portal to another dimension," mused Harry excitedly.

' "I haven't really started concentrating yet," said Stephen, grinning.

'Just then, Harry shouted at me, "Quick! Grab it! There's a face on the screen!"

'All eyes surveyed the screen. A face was forming, as if coming through into the circle from behind the screen. It was a man's face. He had a beard. It looked like Dr Kahn. He smiled! A cheeky grin. Then he disappeared.

'I had clicked the mouse at just the right moment and caught the circle of white light on the screen. But when we printed it out, there was no face, just the light. (The picture is now on display at the Danbury Healing Clinic.) Although disappointed not to have a picture to show the inevitable army of sceptics, all five people in that room knew that a major first had just occurred: the face of a person from another dimension of reality, another world, had been seen with modern technology...

'I have already suggested that other worlds could occupy the same space as ours, but operate on much higher vibrations or frequencies. Is it feasible that, if it were Dr Kahn on the screen, he might have lowered his own vibration or operating frequency to precisely the right one to be picked up by Harry's machine?'

These metaphysical or paranormal applications of PIP are wholly unintentional. Nevertheless, there was little doubt in our minds that a man like Stephen Turoff, who actually sees with his own eyes what PIP makes visible to the rest of the world, could teach us a great deal.

At Stephen's clinic it was inevitable that we would meet other people who would be fascinated by the PIP technology. One of these was Dr Digish Patel, a dental surgeon who was intrigued by what he had heard about PIP and had come to see it for himself, together with his partner, Dr Travessa Newton.

Both have since visited the PIP clinic on more than six occasions, Dr Patel to have PIP scans and Dr Newton to observe. In

December 1997, Dr Patel kindly provided his impressions, which were written up in association with Dr Newton:

A DENTIST'S EXPERIENCES OF PIP

'I first found out about PIP when visiting Stephen Turoff at the Danbury Healing Clinic. It was explained to me that, in simple terms, the energies of the different parts of the body are represented on the PIP scanner in different colours and patterns according to the health of each organ/body part. I was keen to see what possibly might be imbalanced or needing attention after a few sessions with Stephen.

'My personal experience of PIP is that it has been extremely accurate in the diagnosis of various problems which I had already suspected existed. Musculo-skeletal problems in my back and left hip showed up on initial photographs.

'I had suffered with lower back pain for many years. This was caused by repeatedly having to twist to the left while at work, one of the drawbacks of a left-handed dentist having to use a right-handed dental unit. After changing jobs, and therefore dental units, I felt that the condition had improved.

'This was confirmed at my most recent PIP session. PIP showed temporo-mandibular joint (TMJ) facial muscle tension, as well as neck and shoulder tension. This was related to stress at work and made me realize the need for relaxation and "switching off" after a hard day. Colonic problems, for which I was already being treated by Stephen Turoff, also showed up on PIP.

'Certain symptoms such as sluggishness, feeling cold and difficulty in losing weight made me suspect that I might have an underactive thyroid. PIP confirmed this and prompted me to start a course of kelp tablets. Recent PIP scans show an improvement in thyroid activity.

'From a medical/dental perspective it can be seen that PIP could play an important role in the holistic diagnosis of an individual. PIP does not only show disease which is already present, it also shows up areas of the body where disease might manifest itself at a future date.

'For example, a person with a family history of diabetes could be regularly screened by PIP to check for underfunction of the pancreas. This could be dealt with *before* diabetes manifested itself.

'This form of rapid, non-invasive diagnosis of medical and dental problems could lead to the improved treatment of individuals. Disease could be caught in its very early stages, when treatment is usually much quicker, easier and cheaper.'

In regard to this last comment, Harry often expresses his wish that his scanners will one day be in every doctor's surgery and hospital clinic. Or even mortuary...

DEATH: END OR TRANSITION?

A Monday morning. Harry's wife Eileen was on the telephone, so it was he who answered the door.

'Good morning, Jane. Come in,' he said. 'I've got something really interesting to tell you. The most marvellous opportunity for research has come up. We've been invited to film the energies in a mortuary.'

My face must have shown my surprise. It's not the kind of thing you expect to hear first thing on a Monday morning.

'That's fantastic, Harry. How on Earth was it arranged?'

'Well, a very open-minded coroner, a professor of pathology in southern Europe, has heard about my work of analysing energy fields around the living body. He wants to see whether PIP can show the energy leaving the body at the time of death. Of course, that would be extremely difficult to arrange, but we can certainly look at the energy soon after death and post-mortem changes.'

'He sounds like an enlightened man. What do you know about him?' I asked.

'He's said to be an unusual pathologist in that he approaches the body in a very humane way, not just as a clinical object. He tries to find out what has happened to a person spiritually as well as physically. Not only that, Jane, but he senses that there are a lot of spiritual presences in the mortuary he is working in at the moment, more so than in any other he has worked in. Perhaps PIP can pick something up.'

A few weeks later Harry and I, equipped with camera and laptop computer, flew off to our destination, somewhere in southern Europe. (We have been asked to be discreet about the location and the name of the coroner given the sensitive nature of the subject matter.)

We stayed with the colleagues who had arranged the visit and learned that many of the people who worked in the mortuary had reported seeing strange shadows and figures, especially in the older part of the building.

The day for filming arrived. We had to get up bright and early, before the birds in fact, to get to the mortuary before the coroner started his busy day. Surprisingly, despite some apprehension, I had slept well. Although I had seen death many times during my nursing career, I had never grown accustomed to it. Harry, too, was a little apprehensive.

We did not have to wait long outside the mortuary before the coroner arrived. My nerves were soothed by his appearance. He had the most incredibly kind soft brown eyes. Through our interpreter, Harry reiterated that the research would be conducted as ethically as possible. All films would be confidential and, out of respect for the deceased and their families, under no circumstances would faces be shown to outside parties.

We were told that four corpses had been brought to the mortuary in the last 12 hours. The coroner had asked that none of the bodies be kept in the fridge, just left as 'natural' as possible. He took us along to a large room where they would be laid out and where we would be able to film. On the way there he explained that the first body we would see would be that of a young man who had died only a few hours before following a road traffic accident.

We were to film 'normally' and then run the footage through the PIP system later. This was to allow greater movement around the room, as being attached to the computer would have greatly restricted the angle of shots. The disadvantage of this was that we would not be able to see the energies as we filmed.

Harry and I had discussed the many theories of how the soul or consciousness leaves the body. Some say that at the moment of death your whole life flashes before you. This occurs as the memories stored in your 'energetic' body pass before your eyes as your consciousness leaves through the crown chakra on the top of your head, also known as the point of Shiva.

We arrived at the 'viewing' room. There, on a long wooden table, looking as though he had been waiting for us, was a young man. He appeared to be asleep. It seemed to us that there was still something of his 'essence' remaining. The surgeons had obviously tried to save him as he had wound dressings taped over the left side of his lower ribs. I said a silent prayer for him. Harry told me later that he had done the same. With a great feeling of sadness, I began filming.

'Remember to get a view of the crown, for the point of Shiva,' said Harry.

I did as instructed and held the camera steady, pointing it at the top of the head. Then, starting at the feet, I slowly panned up the body, pausing for a few seconds over the area of the large intestine, where bacterial activity and peristalsis (muscular contractions of the intestines) occur for a while after death.

'Make sure you get a wide-angle panoramic view to encompass the body and the energy surrounding it,' reminded Harry, 'and get some footage of the walls and ceiling. We may see energetic emanations hovering above the body.

'Think of those reports of near-death-experiences where people report floating above their bodies. Perhaps that happens transiently after death. We may see evidence of it when we run the film through the PIP system.'

I also thought of how the young man had died, suddenly and unexpectedly. In such cases it is said that the consciousness is in a state of shock and that it takes a while for the person to 'move on'. Perhaps that was why we sensed a 'living presence' around this young man?

We went on to film all four deceased in the same way. Two of them, a man and a woman, had died approximately 24 hours before, from drug overdoses. In addition, there was an elderly gentleman who had suddenly expired 12 hours previously. He had been out at his local coffee bar chatting with friends when, mid-sentence, he had collapsed and died.

Surveying the bodies, Harry shared his thoughts on rigor mortis:

'I have pondered on why nature has provided us with rigor mortis and why it is transient. I have a theory that for a short time after death the body is still very viable: the "vehicle of vitality" is still present although the consciousness has gone. Therefore the Lord has provided a safety valve to stop mischievous entities from coming in and taking over the body. Rigor mortis provides a protection mechanism until everything is properly dead.

'Places such as this mortuary, hospitals, battlefields, places of execution, old people's homes and so on may be established collection points where the departing souls are met at the beginning of their new journey.

'In medieval times people talked about the angel of death. I believe that these "collectors" are angelic presences, not sinister ones. They are there to guide us to the light. They would be appropriate to the particular person. For example, if someone dies on a battlefield, their collector might well be dressed as an officer. Alternatively these collectors may appear as clergymen of the country or denomination of the deceased. This would be something familiar to help reduce the shock to the system.

'It is a well-known fact that many people nearing death call out to deceased loved ones and appear to hold conversations with them. We are not conditioned to expect this, although it is a very common phenomenon. Perhaps if something happens often enough, it should be considered an aspect of reality and we should teach our children about it.'

Wc had to wait until our return to England to process the film through the PIP system. Seeing the film brought back the same sadness we had felt at the mortuary. Harry comments on the footage as follows:

'Post-mortem changes were the most advanced in the man who had committed suicide by drug overdose, where we could see that the body was bloated. This bloating had been caused by the accumulation of gas, a by-product of bacterial activity in the blood and gut. His skin was turning black.

'PIP showed a very low-grade energetic pattern similar to those I have seen when looking at bacterial growth in Petri dishes. This low-grade energy appeared as very dark red patterns where the toxins were high. Black patterns were also seen on PIP. Black denotes that life force is absent.

'Looking first at the energy configurations nearest to the physical, we noted that there appeared to be more residual energy around the young man and the elderly gentleman. Then, looking above their bodies, we noted unexpected configurations of energy, approximately the same length and width as the physical body, reaching up to about four feet above it. These configurations did not seem to be present above the other two deceased. This energy expanded and contracted, appeared as golden pulsating light and was most vibrant above the young man. We also saw what appeared to be faint echoes of meridian energy channels on him. They were, however, pale reflections of the vibrant streams seen in living subjects.

'Hovering near the ceiling, above the elderly gent, we saw an unusual shape. It looked like a head and torso, only more ovoid in shape.

'At the end of the young man's bench was a small metal table. On this we saw another energy configuration which could not be explained by normal light patterns. It appeared to resemble a figure sitting in a cross-legged position, gazing at the lifeless form on the bench. Of course, some will say that you can make patterns out of wallpaper if you look hard enough. However, the figure was very distinctive.'

ANGELOS: A COLLECTOR OF SOULS?

The images captured in the mortuary are certainly open to interpretation. They include what appear to be faces on pillars and butterfly configurations on a blank wall. The butterfly is said to symbolize transformation from confinement in the chrysalis to the relative freedom of 'flight' after death.

However we interpret most of the images, there remains one pattern from Harry's research to date which many who have seen it think is showing something significant. This is the picture of what Harry believes could be a benevolent being whom we have affectionately christened 'Angelos' *(see plate section)*. Harry explained this manifestation to us:

'As you know, Angelos was not recorded at the mortuary. Soon after our return I was doing an intensive study of the mortuary footage, especially of the figure sitting cross-legged on the table near to the body of the young man. I then went on to run a systems check on the PIP in readiness for the next day, as I always do.

'One of the checks involved taking a picture of the blank screen which is in my office to make sure that the camera was working. Still with this cross-legged figure in mind, wondering if perhaps he was a guide or a collector, I suddenly noticed a portal of light opening on the screen and patterns appearing. Without thinking, I instinctively clicked the mouse button and captured the image.

'It didn't take much imagination to see the priest-like figure of Angelos, holding a staff which I think bears a crucifix. A vortex of energy, a trumpet-like projection, could be seen coming out of his mouth, as if he were trying to speak. This, of course, is open to discussion!

'I was astonished by this appearance and can only be grateful for the experience and insight. However, in science, such things have to be repeatable. Unfortunately at this time I have not been able to replicate these conditions.

'One can only hope that future developments in my PIP system, with higher and higher ranges of signals being captured and observed, will result in a video connection to other worlds. One day we may even have an inter-dimensional Internet.'

An important aspect which always arises during any discussion of the nature of 'other dimensions of reality' is that of time. The nature of time has always fascinated humanity. Early on, the natural world provided measurements such as night and day and the passing of seasons. Humans have since developed different concepts of time. Aboriginal people in Australia have Dream Time, for example. Since the advent of the mechanical measurement of time we run our world according to a standardized system on which we can all agree. But how often do we pause to consider the true nature of this concept we call 'time'?

CRYSTAL TIME WARPS?

Harry Oldfield has long been intrigued by time and its many implications. Soon after the invention of his first opto-crystal therapy device, which employed a red diode to pulse light through a red crystal, Harry began to get unusual feedback from his patients. Many reported that they experienced what Harry calls 'time discrepancies' when using the device. This set him thinking. Much later, when the development of relevant technology permitted, Harry introduced a blue-light opto-crystal therapy unit, which pulsed blue light through blue crystals.

In August 1997, we acquired one of these blue-light devices from Michael Fitzpatrick, the school's electro-crystal accessory designer. Then Harry just happened to mention he had been doing some experiments with the blue-light system with a friend of his, a young woman who was soon to go to Cambridge to study physics. Harry had a hunch and he and his young colleague decided to put it to the test:

'The idea was that the opto-crystal devices can somehow slow down or speed up time for the person whose energy field is worked on in relation to someone who is not in the same field.

'We have had a number of reports from patients who experienced what might be called "time discrepancies" whilst attached to the machines. So we tried an experiment with the blue diode light machine. And the results were incredible. Time appeared to pass faster for the person in the localized field by up to five seconds per minute in one experiment.

'It might be to do with something called "light tunnelling", which in this case would have involved light travelling faster than the accepted speed of light for the person in the field. In effect, photons were going backwards in time.'

Harry saw that we were having trouble with this one.

'Why don't we try it?' he suggested matter of factly.

'OK,' we readily agreed.

'Right, Grant, you come out into the hall by the big clock. Jane can take the other watch.'

We trooped down the passage into the hallway, following along behind Harry in a now familiar procession. At the end of the hall, the big clock ticked away.

'Now, Grant, you must point the red-light beam coming from the opto-crystal unit onto both your arm and the clock. Jane, you and I should stand well away from Grant's energy field.

'As I have explained, the blue-light machine made local-ized time go faster for the person in the field. If my theory is correct, the red diode light machine will slow Grant and the clock down relative to anyone outside the field. This means, Jane, that the watch should gain time relative to Grant and the clock. Are we ready?'

We certainly were. We waited for the clock to reach the vertical and then Grant started shining the red light on both his arm and the clock. The watch was started at the same time.

As the seconds ticked by, Grant got ready to stop the machine exactly on the vertical and the watch was stopped at the same instant. We all looked at the watch. 'There we are!' exclaimed Harry. 'The watch has gained one-and-a-half seconds against the clock.'

Ever keen to ensure that scientific method is observed, Harry told us that he would be conducting a number of experiments with identical stop watches, switching them around, using con-trol time-pieces and so on, before he could be absolutely sure that the time-alteration effect was real.

'The trouble is,' he said, smiling, 'I *want* it to be true. And that's a problem in science. So I will have to do a lot more work before I am willing to conclude anything.'

He suggested we should try this time experiment independently.

'If it is a replicable effect, what are the implications?' we asked him.

'Well, if we could build a big enough generator, who knows what might happen? For a start, physics has already proved that light travels more coherently through crystals. And we are pulsing light through crystals to achieve the effect you have just witnessed.

'Of course, it was some time ago that a group of physicists used two atomic clocks to prove Einstein's theory that time passes differently relative to the speed a person is travelling.

'They took one of the atomic clocks on an airliner and left a control clock on the ground in a fixed position. The clock in the aircraft had lost time relative to the clock on the ground. This difference was very small, but it proved Einstein's theory of relativity.

'In a life-threatening medical situation, say, open-heart surgery, we may be able to slow the brain down so that every molecule of oxygen is utilized better. In industry, we could shine the red light on a jet engine to prolong working life. Time may be elastic. It might flow like water, with ripples coming at us from the past or occasional backwash from the future.

'We may be able to warp time. We may be able to travel back to a different past in a parallel universe or go forward into the future of this universe. The thing is that none of the theorists really knows. Nor do I, of course. Someone has actually got to find a way of sending consciousness through time to find out the truth.'

'Do you think you might be able to actually achieve time travel with your opto-crystal generators, Harry?'

'At the moment I don't know ... but I'm certainly on the case.'

THE TRAVELLING MIND

Some estimates suggest that 90 per cent, or even more, of the brain is not apparently being used for day-to-day living. And, despite the apparent complexity of a bio-mechanical brain and nervous system in which signals travel like electricity down wires to and from a central computer, Harry Oldfield is not at all convinced that this mechanism can account for the variety and scope of our very short and limited human Earthly experience, let alone our universal one.

Harry believes that the brain acts like a transceiver, a radio-communications device for 'talking' to each of the cells in the body. In this way, the brain, with its two halves, becomes a 'di-pole transceiver' and the cells, with their DNA double-helix 'aerials', are able to send and receive messages to and from the command centre.

In this scenario, not only do signals travel down 'wires' but are also radiated through space-time like waves, and this helps us to function and have an experience on Earth.

You may or may not accept the intriguing possibility that the brain and body cells could operate on both a mechanistic (wiring) and an energistic (radio) level, but, as Harry says, 'If we accept that our brain can send radio messages to each of our cells, we can more easily accept that we might radiate messages to each other.'

Many have speculated that Harry's ideas and investigations may one day lead to a more scientific understanding of phenomena such as clairvoyance, telepathy, ESP and so on.

Harry continues this theme:

'And if we accept that we might send these radio-communications through space-time to each other, why shouldn't we be able to pick up the broadcasts from the One Universal Mind, the ultimate broadcast source, which I would call God?

'Perhaps, through learning to listen to these broadcasts, we would be able to access the totality of knowledge much more easily than we can by limiting ourselves to the Earth-dwelling, bio-mechanical, electrically wired, physical model of the human being.'

It is clear that the concepts of brain, mind and consciousness are central to Harry's thinking. He considers that the mind may be:

'... capable of travelling at infinite velocity. In this state, our consciousness would be raised to the "purest state of being", a condition in which that part of ourselves we know and understand as "I" exists in all realms at all times and in all states of matter, energy and consciousness at the same moment.

'Time becomes irrelevant because, at infinite velocity, we have broken all light barriers and crossed all frontiers simultaneously. In this state of pure being, we become one with the Oneness.

'But what are the implications of trying to achieve infinite velocity? At our physical, visible Earth-body level we know we are a vibrating mass of congealed energy or frozen light. Theoretically, we can become invisible to normal sight by vibrating each of our particles beyond the range of human eye perception. But even if we could do this, in order to continue to be a being with recognizable form, all our particles would still have to hang together, albeit at the higher vibration we somehow managed to experience.

'In other words, in order to maintain coherent form, our base molecular structure, electrical processes and so on, all have to stay in geographical proximity to each other in the same space-time place-moment. If we tried to achieve infinite coverage, to be "everywhere at once" in a physical sense, our bits and pieces would be so widely spread that we would quite literally be all over the place.

'And, rather ironically, we would also be "nowhere at all", as no one else would recognize us as us and therefore we would not, in the normal sense at least, exist as an entity.

'However, at our mind level we can achieve a state of infinite velocity and still be ourselves. The mind has no boundaries. I believe that this might be what is meant by the notion that we are made in God's image – we are each a miniature representation of the One Universal Mind. In this scenario, our physical Earth-body is a sort of vehicle for limiting our experiences rather than being a material representation or likeness of our Creator.'

This limiting physical vehicle concept may be true for all beings. Each living being experiences a different physical reality – bats, say, have sonar to guide them around and moles have no eyes at all but instead sense with their nose and whiskers. Harry asks:

'Is it so much of a jump to accept that the crystal-dwelling life-forms have similarly distinct design adaptations and so live here both with us and not with us, as it were?

'Even though these crystal-dwelling photonic beings do appear to be here with us, they are ordinarily invisible and we had to wait for the development of an instrument before the majority of us could see them. The same could hold true for beings from other planets or realms in the universe. If such things exist there is no reason at all why they should be detectable by our very limited human sensors. In fact logic and chance would predict otherwise.'

To understand just how limited the information available to us is, we should perhaps take a brief look at how our natural senses work. Harry says:

'In our environment all things that appear to be solid to our eyes – and thus physically "real" – are in fact composed of congealed light or condensed energy. Moving light bounces off matter, which is itself light frozen in a particular space-time place-moment, and information signals are the result.

'The eyes of observers such as humans are designed to pick up a certain very limited range of these information signals. Cells called "rods" respond to the brightness of the light and others called "cones" detect its component colours. Cones cannot perform well at low light levels.

'Sounds are waves or vibrations which travel through substances such as air and can be detected by mechanisms in our ears. We hear sound because the ear amplifies the vibrations, channelling them towards sensitive detectors in the inner ear. We know that other creatures (and our instruments) hear a greater range of sounds than we do. Once again, our vehicle of experience seems to be designed with a built-in limitation.

'Smells are the brain's response to molecules of chemical substances which can be detected by sensors in our noses. These chemicals dissolve in the nasal mucus inside the nose and stimulate hair-like endings on a bulb. Smell is processed by the part of the brain that also deals with memory and emotions.

'Tastes – bitter, sweet, salty and sour – are detected by bud receptors on our tongues. Chemicals dissolved in saliva reach these taste receptors through pores. Taste and smell work together to help us identify flavours.

'Our fifth sense, that of touch, is aided by sensors all over the outer covering of the body, the skin.

'So, the perceived world is merely a limited range of information signals received by our senses and transmitted by various ingenious means to our brain which then converts them into an understandable reality. Thus, the brain is the control centre, overseeing and integrating the internal and external experience of each human being.

'Co-ordination of skilled movement, behaviour and emotion, speech and senses enabling us to see, hear, smell, taste and touch this environment in which we find ourselves all appear to be some of the functions of this clever biological computer. By storing this information in its memory, the brain allows you to remember the past so that you can compare it with the present and make decisions about the future.

'So, on one level, the brain seems to be a sort of biological central computer designed to assist your mind to move your body around in a visible physical environment – and from these interactions we all have day-to-day experiences. I am trying to invent instruments which will help more of us experience more of the invisible universe.'

In order to free himself of the normal constraints that he feels might put limits on our thinking, Harry is fond of using the analogy of a travelling mind without the limitations imposed by physical form.

He also allows for the possibility that the conscious mind may travel without the body, as in reported cases of 'out of body' experiences. Harry adds:

'And then, of course, there is the question of whether the conscious mind travels to "somewhere else" after death and if so, how, why and under what conditions? Then there is the question of reincarnation. Is it at least feasible that our consciousness, the software, if you like, might return in another body, the hardware, to gain further experience of the whole?'

These and other questions are just the thin end of the wedge that is Harry Oldfield's field of enquiry. To get an idea of the scope of Harry's investigations, let's travel with him on an imaginary journey with our minds to the largest and smallest, nearest and furthest reaches of the visible and invisible universe, which has so fascinated him throughout his life ...

'First, imagine you are floating in space with the potential ability to perceive everything in any way you choose. You look down at yourself, to get your bearings. OK, that looks fairly familiar.

'Now, you look to the left. There, to your amazement, stretching out into the distance are all the smaller things than yourself, lined up in descending order. The line-up starts with things like dogs and chairs and goes on down through small mammals to blades of grass and insects and grains of sand. You wonder for just a moment how conscious these things are of themselves, of being "I". You keep perceiving until you get to the limit of the unaided eye, the humble crab louse.

'But, because you are travelling in your mind, you can now

switch into aided sight mode. You materialize a microscope and look through the viewfinder. There in the round window you can perceive a single-celled protozoan, which is about a tenth of a millimetre across. This is the simplest of independent living creatures. It is many, many times smaller than your human frame.

'You continue on down until you reach the limits of visible light. The different wavelengths of this light can be sensed by your eyes and turned into information by your brain. You are at the aided sight barrier, on the border of the invisible universe.

'You discard the 'scope, shrink into micro-mind mode and pass over the border. Viruses, the simplest of dependent living creatures, come up on the perception horizon. Molecules appear, getting smaller and smaller and smaller still. Downwards you travel.

'Atoms are vibrating ahead. Things are a little hazy at this level. You are in the realm where the difference between matter and energy is hard to perceive. If you travel on down you will meet, at least according to current theory, the atomic nuclei composed of protons and neutrons ... and then the electrons which complement each nucleus. Here, at the very limits of human knowledge, are the sub-atomic particles called quarks. If you accept that these are particles, that they are "material things occupying space", these quarks carry a third of a charge each and depend on each other for their existence. I call this the "sub-atomic Trinity".

'At this level, the "limit of perception" is accompanied by a constant companion, the "limit of description". These tiny "things" have been variously described as "pinched up space", "congealed light" and "frozen energy". All we know for certain is that, relative to the human body, they are very, very, very small.

'Suddenly, you get the urge to grow back to your original Earth-body size and imagine it to be so. You look down at yourself once again to re-establish your bearings.

'Now you look to the right. There, stretching out into the distance are all the things bigger than yourself, lined up in ascending order. The line-up starts with things like cars and elephants and goes on up through trees and houses to parks and cities. The largest cities are about 30 miles across. The length of one of these great gatherings of human beings and their dwellings approaches half of one per cent of our planet's diameter in size.

'Onwards and upwards you go. Countries, continents, the moon, the Earth, other planets. Now you reach the sun, a great fiery ball many times the size of the Earth. But it is a very ordinary star, others are much larger.

'You travel on to perceive the nebulae. These masses of hydrogen gas and grains of dust are scores of light years across. Their size is equivalent to the distance between the Earth and the nearest star. But you can still travel on to perceive still bigger things.

'Galaxies come into view. These huge assemblages of stars, gas and dust are bound together by gravitation. Many are 100,000 light years across. In terms of relative size, a galaxy is to a human what a human is to an atom. Further along your journey you meet the clusters of galaxies.

'Then, finally, you come across a supercluster of galaxies. You can hardly miss one! They are the largest known collections of matter in the universe. In the presence of this vast supercluster, you suddenly feel a little insignificant.

'You reflect for a moment on the fact that if you were standing on Earth rather than travelling with your mind you would not be able to see most of these things. Suddenly, you realize that, from your limited Earth perspective, these big things are as much a part of the invisible universe as the little things.

'Most of this enormity is not available to your sight without another instrument, a telescope. You become aware of how important scientific instruments are to the amount of this invisible universe that you have access to now and how important they will become in the future for space travel and perhaps even inter-dimensional exploration.'

So, in a sense then, the human being is piggy-in-the-nearly-middle of the big and little things in the universe. A great vantage point, you might conclude, from which to set off on a journey of exploration in that wonderful vehicle of experience – your mind – to the strange and mysterious worlds of *Harry Oldfield's Invisible Universe*.

THE YOUNG SCIENTIST

'You cannot solve a problem with the same type of thinking that gave rise to it.'

ALBERT EINSTEIN

H ARRY'S mother Juliet grew up in India, but at the time of Independence, in 1947, there was much danger in that troubled land and she and her younger sister were sent home by their mother, Esther Cornby. They arrived in Liverpool and were taken to a convent in the city. Their mother joined them a year later, having had to accept unreasonable terms when disposing of the family's assets in India. They were consequently reduced to a much humbler life than they had previously enjoyed, but they were together, healthy and happy once again. They moved to a rather small but comfortable house in Ashton-under-Lyne, Greater Manchester, and 17-year-old Juliet went dancing and met Frank, her future husband.

Frank was 10 years older than his dancing partner, but it was love at first sight and the age difference presented no impediment to their marriage, which took place a year later, in 1952. Frank was a down-to-earth, solid, honest man. He worked on the railways and his wife soon found work as a telephonist. They planned to save a little money, enough to buy a house and start a family, but when Juliet became pregnant, necessity presented itself a little earlier than they had planned and they decided to move to London, where there were more opportunities and better pay. Frank started work on the buses for London Transport and soon the family's policy of spend some, save some enabled them to buy a house in North Kensington. A little while later, at a hospital in Paddington, little Harold Oldfield was born. It was March 1953.

There was an early emphasis on learning in the Oldfield household, which was quite unusual for a working-class family at that time. Frank Oldfield had had his education interrupted by the war and had left school early. He was determined that Harold and the identical twins, Kenneth and Phillip, who soon followed him into the world, would have better opportunities. This fostering of learning resulted in three brothers who became, respectively, a scientist/inventor, a research biochemist at Cambridge and a gourmet chef who runs his own catering business.

'Dad thought science was a solid subject so we were all encouraged to study it,' Harry began explaining to us. 'One of my brothers ended up as a chef, of course, but Dad would have said that good food is the *art* of chemistry. I got on well with my brothers. We were a close family.'

On turning five, Harry started at Oxford Gardens, a school in North Kensington. He has always had a great interest in 'all living things and how the world worked' and this must have shone through to many of his teachers, who gave him lots of encouragement. The bright and bouncy little lad was a joy to his headmistress. He would turn up at her office door wearing his long baggy shorts with a toothy smile.

'Hello, Harold, did you want to see me?' she would tease him. She knew what he really wanted – not to see her but the pet squirrel and budgerigar that lived in her room.

'Not really, Miss,' he would reply sheepishly. 'I've come to see the animals.' At least he was open and honest, qualities that have remained with him to the present day.

After young Harold had seen the animals, he would sit and talk to the headmistress. She treated him like a little man and they would talk about all manner of things. She told Harry's parents that he was 'gifted' and they were quite happy to believe it. To encourage him, they saved up and bought him some tropical fish for his sixth birthday.

'The tank was enormous,' says Harry. He is still enthusiastic about it today. 'And you must remember it was 1959. Nobody else in our street had a tropical fish tank. I was so proud and happy. All my friends came round to have a look. And their parents!'

At home, the young scientist conducted 'experiments'. When he was about eight, he decided he wanted to make a crystal radio set. He had read how to do it in a book and started gathering the materials in the backyard. He constructed a metal aerial to receive the signals from the air and attached it to a metal dustbin. The plan was that the aerial would pick up the signals from the BBC which would travel down to Earth via the dustbin. In between the two was a crystal and electronic circuit arrangement connected to an amplifier to which earphones were attached. The radio waves broadcast by the BBC are 'carrier waves' which transport modulated signals or information about the original sounds. The crystal was imperative. It converted the modulated signals back into the original sounds by vibrating or oscillating in sympathetic resonance with the radio wave.

Having constructed the contraption, the time came to switch it on. 'Hooray, it works!' Harry exclaimed, and subsequently spent many contented hours by the dustbin listening to the BBC.

In line with the value he placed on learning, Frank bought his eldest son a microscope on his tenth birthday. Harry says:

'It was 1963 and to have a microscope at home was unheard of. But once again my parents had found a way to really inspire me in my search for knowledge about how things worked. I would take a blob or a sliver of absolutely anything I could get my hands on and look at it under the microscope. Specks of dust, pond water, slime-mould from trees, you name it, I 'scoped it. That microscope was highly significant. It showed me a whole new unseen world which I didn't know was there. I embarked on an exploration into the unknown which has gripped me ever since. This one gift sparked my greatest passion – unveiling the invisible universe.'

Harry's next great inspiration in his search for knowledge came shortly afterwards when he went to Christopher Wren school and met a new science teacher, Mr Watson:

> 'He treated me like an adult and did nothing but encourage me, even if I made lots of mistakes. I began to read every scientific and technical book I could lay my hands on. Mr Watson noted my enthusiasm and gave me private tutorials in science as well as giving me access to all the chemicals and other things necessary for my experiments. He may have seen some potential in me. He knew I had a microscope at home and he used to give me amoebae, paramecium, euglena, all sorts of things. I used to keep these bits and pieces in small tubes in my top blazer pocket during the day and then take them home to have a look at under the microscope.'

Within a year, aged just 12, Harry had come up with his first commercially viable scientific invention ... which is still in use today! The project began when Harry decided he wanted to feed his tropical fish their natural diet of whole shrimps, rather than the brine shrimp eggs that were supplied in pet food shops. He wrote off to the company which supplied the shrimp eggs, asking whether whole adult shrimps were available. The company wrote back informing him that they were not, as acquiring the wild algae which the shrimps fed on and which helped them to grow was not commercially viable and that native algae killed them. All in all there was no suggestion the company could offer.

Harry has never understood the word 'impossible' and the reply certainly did not discourage him. He set about finding a food substance that had cells with the same characteristics as the wild algae. After much searching with the microscope he deduced that yeast cells might be a contender. As an experiment he put the brine shrimp eggs in a container filled with a salt water solution and placed them in his mother's airing cupboard to hatch. Once they had, he began introducing brewer's yeast in minute amounts to the diet of the tiny live shrimps in the hope that they would thrive on it and grow into adults. To him this was a perfectly reasonable possibility. Juliet was not, however, so reasonable when he managed to spill the contents of the bowl onto her underwear! 'She had shrimps in her knickers and everything,' Harry remembers with boyish relish. 'Luckily, after a few days in the dog house, Mum let me continue with the experiment.'

After an enormous amount of trial and error, Harry finally got the formula of yeast, volume of water, strength of salt solution, time period and temperature right and managed repeatedly to produce adult shrimp from eggs in the airing cupboard. He explains his approach:

'You see, I've never really been a theoretical scientist, I'm a hands-on, nuts and bolts, make it work and function type really. Theory is obviously necessary, but it's just not my main thing. This sometimes gets me into trouble with orthodox scientists who like it all nice and tidy. But for me, I learned early on that doing it by the book and accepting that something is impossible because it hasn't been done before or doesn't fit the accepted theory is just a recipe for failing before you've even started. I can only speak for myself, but I think that sort of attitude gets in the way and stifles the spirit of true innovation.'

Perseverance is another quality that appears to be required of the innovative inventor. Thomas Edison is reported to have tried 999 times before finally getting the light bulb right. He suffered derision with each attempt, but something kept him going. Harry seems to have the same gritty determination.

Eventually, Harry sent the fish-food company a complete report, innocently including all the details of his experimental procedures. The scientists at the company carried out their own confirmatory experiments and eventually wrote back in glowing terms. 'They sent me £100!' exclaimed Harry. 'And in the mid-sixties that was an awful lot of money, especially to a 12-year-old. My parents were very proud of me. As a thank you to them for being so wonderful, I asked if we could spend the money on a family holiday. We had a great time.'

Older and wiser now, Harry reflects on what might have been the financial result of this invention if he had sent only the end result of his experiments to the company and negotiated a percentage royalty before giving everything away:

'Less than a year later, that company was selling freeze-dried adult shrimps in aquarium and pet shops. They must have made a packet from it. And they're still commercially available and going strong today. I could always do with more research funds for my work. Oh well, *c'est la vie!*'

'The Shrimp King', as he became known, continued his scientific studies and his inventing throughout his school years, before being accepted as a temporary trainee teacher at the tender age of 17 and going on to the University of London, where he read biology and physics.

A major event in Harry's life, which prompted him to change his whole outlook, presented itself when he was 19. Along with other trainee teachers Harry was asked to go to a school for children with special needs. These children had major disabilities. To get to the school, Harry was driving down Hounslow East High Street in his very old and battered Austin. He stopped at some traffic lights and began to think about the day ahead and the little ones he was due to work with. Suddenly, a loud voice in the car said, 'You are going to see my children. Look after them well.'

Who said that? thought the startled young man. He checked the radio to see if it was on, then checked the windows to make sure no one had shouted in through them. Meanwhile the lights had turned green and he was causing a bit of a hold up.

'I pulled away, but had to stop to collect my thoughts,' he recalls today. 'I must admit that at the time I thought I might be audio hallucinating.'

After a little while, Harry settled down and was able to continue on his journey. At the school the trainees were greeted by the headmistress and the project leader. They were split into groups and allocated different classes. The headmistress made it clear that she expected them to report back at lunchtime on their experiences, feelings and findings.

Harry's group was asked to observe a class of Down's Syndrome children. These children were particularly affectionate and Harry felt slightly awkward when they began to come up to him, stretch out their hands and say, 'We love you.' One of Harry's friends teased him gently: 'What kind of aftershave are you wearing, Oldfield?'

This rapport between the young trainee teacher and the children continued to develop throughout the class as he helped them with their reading and other work. Harry found himself enjoying the experience far more than he had imagined he would.

At lunchtime the trainees squeezed into a small office. Being quite tall, Harry made his way to the back and half-sat on the windowsill. The window overlooked the playground and Harry could see the children he had just met and they could see him. Teacher and children exchanged waves. The young man was profoundly touched. He sent out a silent prayer: 'God, if it was you who spoke to me in the car, show me how I can help these children.'

Meanwhile, the headmistress had been talking about the shortage of voluntary help at the summer school. 'We run this during the holidays to relieve the stress on parents and...' she broke off mid-sentence. 'But I don't suppose we can hope for any sort of support from young men who spend all their time looking out of the window, can we?'

Harry was startled from his private thoughts. Quickly recovering, he realized the way forward. 'Actually,' he began, 'I would really like to do something with the children in the holidays.'

The headmistress looked a little shocked, but soon relaxed and smiled. 'Well, young man, I'm sure that will be very much appreciated.'

Having reflected at length on the voice in the car, the silent prayer to God and the immediate answer, Harry began to think more seriously about what life was about. At the summer school he spent a few weeks helping with art groups, sports and other lessons. He recalls that it was one of the best periods of his life.

'Through this whole experience God became a reality to me rather than something I had read or heard about. I picked up the Bible and began to read it properly. I was especially drawn to the passages in which Christ performed healing. Almost immediately I identified very personally with the mission of healing the sick. But even though I became a committed Christian, I understood that not everybody believed in Jesus as a prophet or as the Son of God. But I do think that people of any faith, or even of no faith, can identify with the healing mission of the historical figure of Jesus. Even at a down-to-earth level, Jesus the man appears to have been all good and no bad, a sort of perfect model for anyone to seek to emulate.

'Of course, I had no idea at the time that things would go as they did. I wanted to help and heal people, but my whole sphere of knowledge and interest was science. It wasn't until much later that I was able to combine my scientific knowledge with my desire to heal people.'

Harry went on to obtain his degree and then his Diploma of Education. He really wanted to indulge his passion for research and inventing, but common sense, and his father, suggested that a job would be a better idea.

At his first teaching job, Harry was very happy passing on his knowledge and enthusiasm for general science to 11–13-year-olds and for biology and physics to 14–18-year-olds. It wasn't long before he managed to blow up a science laboratory, thereby acquiring the title 'The Mad Professor'. This stuck throughout his teaching career – and it's still pretty apt!

One day Harry was taking a third-form science class in which he was supposed to be teaching the buoyancy of gases. Ever a believer in practical demonstration as a means of teaching and learning, the Mad Professor helped the children to construct a hydrogen balloon measuring about four feet in diameter. With great anticipation they filled the balloon from a small cylinder and attached a small sandbag to the string which was dangling from it.

'OK, scientists, proceed in an orderly fashion outside,' Harry ordered. Teacher and children marched into the playground. Harry stood in the middle of the group explaining what was supposed to happen and why. Suddenly, a gust of wind wrenched the balloon out of his hand. All watched in horror as it was carried off across the playground, heading straight for the headmaster's window.

Crash, the bag hit the window, rattling a pane as it went on its way. Moments later, a very red-faced headmaster threw open the window and bellowed at the culprits below. But all he saw was the innocent faces of a group of children looking up at him like startled rabbits. The guilty fox was rather conveniently obscured behind a wall. As the children watched the balloon's progress, the headmaster followed their eyes and his anger changed to a sort of resignation. He smiled.

'When you do see Mr Oldfield again, would you please ask the Mad Prof. to keep the noise down? Not all of us can have this amount of fun on a Monday morning.'

Harry got the message. Nevertheless, unusual incidents seemed to occur in his vicinity with increasing regularity and this ensured a never-ending interest amongst pupils eager to see what he might do next.

'The thing is,' Harry told us, 'some of the questions they asked made me realize more and more that modern science is missing some very important answers. When the children would ask, "Sir, in the embryo of a human being, why is a toe a toe and not an eye?" I would find myself struggling with a truly satisfactory answer. In my search for the best way to explain such things, I became interested in morphogenetic fields.'

'What are they?'

'Well, the word basically means "origin of form". A morphogenetic field is an idea put forward to explain why natural things keep their shape. If you cut your finger, something organizes the cells to grow and heal exactly where they were before with such precision that you even have the same fingerprint. The same is not true if you cut a man-made object like a piece of paper. It stays cut. I began to think that these "organizing fields of life" were more and more important in the search for answers to the big questions about how everything works.'

'Are we right in saying that much of your work in the diagnosis and treatment of medical conditions was subsequently based on this concept of the "organizing fields of life"?'

'Very much so.'

'Can you explain the idea simply?'

'I'll try. First imagine making a jelly in the shape of a human being: full size, five-and-a-half feet tall, a couple of feet around the middle and so on. You've just conceived an imaginary organizing life field. When using it in connection with people we often call it the human energy field, or HEF for short.

'Now imagine doing the same thing again but this time include a great number of hundreds and thousands – you know, the little multi-coloured sweets – in with the jelly as it sets. What you've got now is a jelly – the organizing field which holds everything together – and the tiny sweets – the physical cells which make up the body that you can see, hear, taste, smell and touch with.

'Now, if we want to influence physical cells, we can do it by poisoning, using chemicals in the form of drugs, by burning, using radiation, or by cutting, using surgery. This is called modern medicine, it is very physical and it basically works on the physical cells.

'To give an example, let's take a case of cancer. Say some of the cells start reproducing out of control. Chemotherapy or radiation may kill the unhealthy cells but may kill some healthy ones as well. Surgery may remove most of them but the surgeon may drop a few and spread the problem to other parts of the whole by the very act of trying to help.

'The thing is, if you disturb any cells, there is a corresponding change in the energy. And if you alter the energy, there is a corresponding change in the cells. And if you get the mix of influencing both the physical cells and the energy template correct you get a much better result than by just doing one or the other.

'I began to believe that the future of medicine lies in treating the energy field with at least as much respect as the physical cells, since it is the organizing HEF which not only holds everything together but also does so much more.'

Having established the importance of energy fields in his own mind, Harry's task later became one of creating a system of diagnosis and treatment. For diagnosis he needed to invent a way of finding where the energy field was distorted or out of shape, and for treatment there needed to be ways of shaping it back to its 'normal', balanced, healthy state.

Meanwhile, back in 1976, Harry was a young schoolteacher just about to experience a major turning point in his life. This was when he saw a Kirlian electro-graph (generally called a 'photograph') of the phantom leaf effect for the first time. The picture was in a book review of the work of two Russians, Semyon and Valentina Kirlian. Harry explained the technique involved:

'The Kirlian technique is a means of creating distinctive "corona" images on photographic paper using high voltages.

'Kirlian equipment itself is very simple. A high voltage coil (producing a pulsing electromagnetic field of between two and 40 kilovolts) is connected to a conductive metal plate. A sheet of photo-sensitive film is placed (emulsion up) on an insulated surface, acting like a sandwich between the charged plate and the photographic film – in effect, protecting the subject from unpleasant sensations. If you switch on the current for one or two seconds under a safe light, the result is a corona discharge of the electrical energy of an object which is recorded on the photo-sensitive film.

'This research into energy fields generated immense interest throughout the Western world when it first emerged from "behind the Iron Curtain" and scarcely any book on the paranormal ever fails to refer to it. Psychic investigators everywhere hoped that at last a physical phenomenon had been uncovered for that elusive non-phenomenon, the human aura. However, I was mainly interested in what the technique might reveal about the organizing fields of life.'

THE 'PHANTOM LEAF' EFFECT. ONE IMAGE (LEFT) SHOWS A CORONA AROUND THE LEAF. THE SECOND (RIGHT) SHOWS THE 'PHANTOM' STILL PRESENT AFTER THE PHYSICAL LEAF HAS BEEN CUT OFF THE STEM.

The accompanying text in the book review explained, very basically, how to make the apparatus that had produced the amazing Kirlian photograph. Inevitably, Harry began to build his own apparatus and, enthused and excited, went on to conduct his own Kirlian research in earnest.

But the next major event in Harry's life was of a more personal nature. While on holiday in Bermuda he met Eileen O'Shea, who was working there. A short while later, they both came back to England and were soon married. Initially they lived with Harry's parents in Northpole Road, North Kensington.

Back at school, Harry had been so keen on the Kirlian idea that he had got his school science club involved as well. This was a club Harry had set up for the emerging group of 'latch-key' schoolchildren. It ran two or three evenings a week and over-subscription was guaranteed by Harry's continuing 'Mad Professor' reputation.

We asked Harry why the phantom leaf effect had had such a profound effect on him.

'Well, if you were looking into the idea that there was an invisible "jelly" of energy which kept physical things in shape, what would be your reaction if you saw a picture that might be evidence of it?' Harry asked.

We realized how central to Harry's work this idea of the template behind the apparent 'form' of physical things was when we began to investigate the phantom leaf for ourselves. Our first surprise was the story of the phantom finger!

ELECTRO

'Comprehend and Copy Nature.'

VIKTOR SCHAUBERGER

I F you accidentally sliced off the top of your finger and left it alone, rather than rushing to hospital to get it stitched and bandaged, would it regrow, complete with fingernail and identical fingerprint?

Most people, including many doctors and scientists, would probably say, 'No way.' Nevertheless, this would apparently be the wrong answer! We, too, had thought, before seeing the evidence Harry showed us, that only reptiles like salamanders had the ability to regrow limbs. But a Central Television programme shown on Channel Four in 1984 outlined the research being done by Professor Bernard Watson of St Bartholomew's Hospital in London. He found that regrowth would occur, but only if the electrical potential flowing into the wound was left unchanged.

'Sewing the finger up appeared to have changed the electrical potential,' reported Professor Watson, 'and though such fingers "healed" in the "normal" way, they did not regrow.'

The origins of the finger regeneration work actually go back to a fateful mistake in the treatment of a young boy in the casualty department at Sheffield Children's Hospital during the early 1970s. He had his wound dressed by the attending doctor, but the usual referral to a surgeon for closure was never made. When the error was discovered a few days later, surgeon Cynthia Illingworth noticed that the finger was regenerating. She decided to leave nature to it and the finger grew back as good as new. Illingworth began 'neglecting' other children and, by 1974, had documented several hundred regrown fingertips, all in children 11 years old or younger. Other clinical studies have since confirmed that young children's fingers cleanly sheared off beyond the outermost joint will invariably regrow perfectly in about three months.

Despite this, the standard treatment in most hospitals would be to stitch the finger. Sadly, 'even the most painstaking surgery gives less than optimal results', according to Dr Robert Becker and Gary Selden in their excellent book *The Body Electric: Electromagnetism and the Foundation of Life* (Quill, 1985).

The Body Electric tells the story of Dr Robert Becker's lifetime of research into the electro nature of living organisms. Friends and colleagues advised him to drop the subject completely, but he went on to find proof of what he called the 'current of injury' in regenerating salamander limbs. Frogs, who could not regenerate, did not have the same electro properties as the regenerating salamanders. As Dr Becker tells us,

'Here was confirmation better than my wildest dreams! Already, in my first experiment, I had the best payoff research can give – the excitement of seeing something no one else had ever seen before.

'I knew now that the current of injury wasn't due to dying cells (i.e. not a mere side-effect as had been previously argued), which were long gone by then. Moreover, the opposite polarities indicated a profound difference in the electrical properties of the two animals, which somehow would explain why only the salamander could regenerate.

'The negative potential seemed to bring forth the all-important blastema. It was a very significant observation, even though the facts had scrambled my neat hypothesis somewhat.'

Dr Becker wrote up his results and submitted his paper to the *Journal of Bone and Joint Surgery*, the most prestigious orthopaedic journal in the world. To his surprise, it was published soon after and was well received in a number of circles.

What Dr Becker wanted to know was where the injury currents came from. Were they related to the nervous system and if so, how? He felt it was unlikely that they started working only after an amputation; they probably existed before. His view was that there must have been a 'pre-existing substratum of direct current activity that responded to the injury':

'Did the voltages I measured really reflect such currents, and did they flow throughout the salamander's body? Did other organisms have them? What structures carried them? What were their electrical properties? What were they doing the rest of the time, before injury and after healing? Could they be used to provoke regeneration where it was normally absent?'

These are some of the questions that Harry Oldfield has also asked. Harry is very interested in the idea of regeneration because, as he said,

'It is central to my notion that there is a template of energy on which the physical molecules are strung. And one of my main objectives is the design of instruments which will help this natural regenerative healing process.

'I've also been in conversation with surgeons about the possibility of regrowing much larger parts of the body, but the main objection I encounter is that, in the case of a leg amputated at the knee for example, the amputee would die from blood loss well before the limb could regrow.

'To overcome this, in sterile conditions, we might fit a contraption over the stump which could create exactly the same pressure as the heart pumping blood and this would get over the blood loss problem.'

We immediately wondered how the leg would know 'how' to regrow. Harry said:

'For a long time since its development in 1989, I have been seeing what might be called "phantom limbs" on my energy field PIP scanner. Many amputees report that they feel pain when someone "walks through" their amputated leg on the train for example. Even though the physical leg is no longer there, the energy counterpart, the original template, still exists. I know it does because we see it on the PIP scanner sometimes.'

'So are you saying that the blueprint of the leg, the original pattern or template, as it were, is still in place after amputation of the physical leg and that the cells would somehow regroup along the same lines as before if they could be stimulated to start the process?'

'Well, it's a bit more complicated than that, but that's the gist of it. Professor Watson's work was explainable in terms of existing scientific laws concerning the electrical nature of cells. *The Dark Side of the Brain* went further, suggesting that the cells do actually communicate with each other by radiating signals, with the main control centre being the brain.

'It is my belief that there are subtle fields of energy which are structural guidelines for size, shape, function and so on. In the case of amputated legs, it might be the adjacent cells on the stump which would broadcast the information to guide regrowth.'

Harry told us that Cynthia Illingworth and her co-worker, Anthony Barker, have measured a negative 'current of injury' leaving the stump of a severed finger. Professor Watson has also found that 'There is a current flowing from the skin on the middle of the finger into the amputation site.'

Harry said that surgeons have had great success with all sorts of electromagnetic devices, especially in the area of bone regrowth. Pete Townsend of the Who was cured of his drug addiction with the help of an electromagnetic box similar to a TENS unit. Harry says, 'This unit could be described as "a small stimulator". The optimum frequency and voltage are fed in to the patient. The real advantage is that the patient can withdraw from the drug because the machine alleviates the symptoms of withdrawal.'

Mr David Wilson, a consultant surgeon in the casualty department of Leeds Infirmary, uses much bigger electromagnetic machines. He says:

'We have used electromagnetism successfully for many things, including pain, dislocations, breakages and ulcers. It has tremendous potential.

'But since the Second World War, the medical companies have done a good job in persuading the medical profession that the only respectable treatment is drug based. I am keen that profession should look at electromagnetism more seriously, especially since there appear to be no side-effects, which of course, we cannot say about drugs.'

Harry wholeheartedly concurs with these sentiments. He told us that some conventional researchers have been trying to introduce electricity and electromagnetism into mainstream practice for many years. In Sweden, for example:

'At the Karolinska Hospital in Stockholm, Professor Bjorn Nordenstrom, a senior consultant radiologist, has devised techniques to destroy cancer tumours with no more than 10 volts of electricity. He has reported considerable successes with both breast and lung cancer.

'One lady had been referred to him for treatment. She was 32 years old and did not want breast removal. Professor Nordenstrom implanted electrodes. After treatment an

X-ray was taken which showed a small white spot in the area of the tumour.'

Professor Nordenstrom explained:

'This is due to calcification around the tumour, which is a natural healing process. Nature takes over the process of healing when we have delivered enough energy. After one week the white spot was much smaller.

'In all healing, electricity is involved, but the key is knowing where and how it comes into it and what principles nature wants us to follow in order to do it best. Mother Nature is in charge and we can only follow her rules.'

Harry says: 'I could not agree more with this. From my experience, nature knows best and we should try to copy her at all times.'

Professor Nordenstrom has reported a very high success rate. In giving his overall view he says: 'I do believe that we should try with electricity a lot more seriously, as this is something we really do know enough about now.'

Dr Robert Beck (not to confused with Dr Robert Becker), one of the world's foremost researchers into electromagnetism, also believes that electromagnetic devices might be the forerunners of the new electronic medicine.

Mr Michael Dwyer, a consultant orthopaedic surgeon at East Birmingham Hospital, has meanwhile been using pulsed radio waves for some time to speed up recovery. When discussing the case of a teenager, Anthony, who is severely disabled by spina bifida, he says:

'Anthony spends his life between bed and a wheelchair. Since Anthony has no sensation in parts of his body, the skin quickly breaks down. Ulcerations can become very large and we just have no conventional means of treating them. But if we put the ulcerated area in a pulsed radio field, the effects are very good.'

Michael Dwyer uses a machine shaped like a big white doughnut, about one foot in diameter. 'This machine sits above the
ulceration and creates a field around it. I'm very impressed
with it.'

The first case of bone healing due to the medical use of
electricity, according to Mr Bob Simonis, another consultant
orthopaedic surgeon, was written up as long ago as 1812. (To put
this in context, Napoleon was retreating from Moscow at that
time.) Bob Simonis explains:

'A surgeon at St Thomas's Hospital in London, John Birch,
was faced with a non-union of a tibia [shin bone] which could
be bent 90 degrees in every direction. A current was passed
into the fracture site by wires which passed through skin.
Six weeks later, the man was allowed to leave, totally cured.'

Bob Simonis himself uses electro help to get the healing going in
some cases:

'A fracture takes six to eight weeks to heal in a normal case.
But in the case of a non-union fracture, that is one that
will not mend, the healing process has stopped working.
Electricity puts energy back into the system, a sort of jump
start for the natural healing mechanism.

'They laughed at me, at first, of course. But then our successes here at the clinic were indisputable. We figure on a
75 to 80 per cent success rate; and that's with people who
have been complete treatment failures with conventional
methods ... I get referrals of "hopeless cases" from all over
the country now.'

Harry continues:

'Bob Simonis uses a machine with two horizontal "dough-
nuts" supported by a vertical bar. A current travels through
the two coils which passes an electromagnetic field between

them. It pulses at about 50 cycles per second. You can hear it ticking when it's turned on.

'If you were to put a wire in the space between the coils and attach it to a torch bulb, the torch would light up by means of a secondary induced current. The same is true with a tibia or other bone – the induced current goes through the bone and causes a healing effect. According to Mr Simonis, his method does take about three months – but it works!

'My healing devices also produce a secondary induced current. But the main difference is that I was able to increase what I call 'the spectrum of healing' by adding the crystal chip oscillators into the electrodes. We were able to open so many more windows of healing opportunity with the crystals that I can scarcely believe it myself.'

Harry is concerned, however, about what he feels is a major problem in medicine:

'At the time of the 1984 Central Television programme, it was reported that the Simonis bone clinic was going to be a victim of the health service cuts and that it was scheduled to close down. Medicine is a big business and sometimes this appears to affect decisions as to which departments remain open and which do not.

'Some commentators, including a number of prominent doctors like those on that television programme, have speculated that the reason for the closure of such departments is that they are too cheap, too effective and do not require expensive drug treatments. I have actually been told by doctors to my face that my devices are too cheap to be any good as medical instruments!'

So, despite the apparent high degree of success of treatments using electricity and electromagnetism, it is worth noting that there are still very few departments offering 'electro-medicine' in hospitals, and those departments that do get up and running appear likely to be shut down just as quickly.

We asked Harry about the reluctance of the medical establishment to accept the electro idea. He said:

'Well, as with everything, the answer isn't that simple. I think that it might be due to the fact that there are really two parts of the "electro" discussion in regard to the human being.

'First, there is *ordinary* energy. There is no doubt that some of our functions depend on electricity – our cells are bathed in a conductive saline solution and electricity flows between the inside and outside of the cell, for example. This is ordinary energy, measurable, gross, physical, "mechanical" if you like.

'Scientists on the whole like this sort of energy because it can be regularly, repeatedly and reliably measured and evaluated with instruments. Medicine is a science of applied biochemistry really and it can accept body electricity quite readily because it is a phenomenon which can be measured and easily understood.

'But there seems to be a problem of acceptance of the "subtle" electro part of ourselves which is much harder to quantify and qualify. This leads on to the second part of the "electro" discussion, which we might call *extraordinary* energy. The energies in this category are to do with forces and fields which cannot be tested and predicted in the way that science tends to prefer.'

Given this steadfast reluctance in the face of the evidence, perhaps it will be left to people 'on the fringe' of conventional medicine – like Harry Oldfield – to provide the subtle electro-healing techniques from which we could all benefit so much in the future.

As we know, Harry saw the first evidence for what might be the energy 'blueprint' which underpins physical matter in 1976 and this led him to start research into Kirlian technology.

We rejoin the story with the school science club he had set up for the 'latch-key kids'.

Harry remembers one particularly memorable event when a couple of third-form girls followed him down the corridor.

'Sir, sir,' they shouted excitedly, waving bromides of the Kirlian pictures they had just developed. 'Look at these pictures, sir, aren't they amazing?'

Harry was hurrying off to lunch but took the time to peruse the pictures. 'What are you talking about, girls? There's nothing there.'

'But that's the point, sir – these are pictures of our school dinners!'

Harry had got the children interested in studying all sorts of foods with their Kirlian cameras and they had undertaken several experiments. Wendy Algar, 14, had eaten 22 sandwiches cut into quarters (five-and-a-half rounds) of white bread in the cause of science and then, on a subsequent occasion, the same amount of brown bread. The increase in energy after eating the brown bread showed up very distinctly on the photograph.

Other remarkable Kirlian photographs were produced showing the differences between organic and processed foodstuffs. Vegetables grown organically showed much more energetic coronas than those grown with the 'help' of pesticides and fertilizers.

Harry also found that different methods of cooking affected the energy. He concluded that, from the point of view of getting the maximum subtle energy benefit from foods, cooking methods 'in declining order of residual Kirlian corona discharge' went from cooking with a wok to steaming, microwave cooking, pressure cooking, prolonged boiling and deep frying, with oven baking bringing up the rear.

Different methods of storage also affected the corona. In the plate section you will find a Kirlian picture of two oranges, one frozen and one fresh. Compare them for yourself. Harry comments:

'Some of these Kirlian pictures of foods were amazing. Subjectively, rather than scientifically, the most beautiful

Kirlian image I have ever seen was of ginseng root. However, my interest in this strange effect did not just lie in its aesthetic or even novelty value for the science class, but in its use as a scientific tool.

'I found it could show stressed metals, poisoned plants, treated foods and, perhaps most importantly, I soon discovered that it had medical diagnostic implications.'

Harry worked on these various projects with his friend and colleague, Ian McGibbon, whose expertise lay in electronics, and a much more sophisticated Kirlian camera was the result. As Harry explained:

'The Kirlian camera takes pictures which show the energy coming out of whatever is being photographed. A Kirlian photograph of a hand shows a "halo" around the hand. I later found that a Kirlian specialist can read a great deal of information about a subject's health, emotions and history by studying it. The process takes minutes and gives the same information as time-consuming conventional diagnostic techniques.

'We first realized the diagnostic potential by chance when we started to photograph the children's hands. Really interestingly, we began to notice subtle differences between the energy fields of those children who were going down with 'flu and those who were not.

'Then I noticed that there appeared to be bright spots on the electro-graph corresponding to the points on the meridians where acupuncturists insert their needles into the hands. In other words, the pattern of the corona of the hand appeared to be able to indicate the state of health of other parts of the body.

'This was very interesting because it pointed towards the rationale behind the treatment of distant organs in acupuncture by inserting needles into apparently unrelated points in the body.

'Not surprisingly, all these findings got me thinking further about the relationship between health and those elusive morphogenetic fields, the invisible organizing fields of life in which energy is said to flow along channels called meridians and configure in whirlpools called chakras. I began to get excited about the possibility that we were actually measuring these fields, flows and configurations with our instruments.'

Eventually, about four years after first seeing that remarkable phantom leaf, Harry had accumulated a vast store of knowledge and research results, all pointing towards the existence of morphogenetic or invisible organizing life fields. He had also become much more convinced that his hypothesis about radiated morphogenetic fields had some validity which might one day be proven.

The improvements in the Kirlian technique soon led to a great deal of interest in the work and a number of lecturing invitations for Harry. One of these winged its way from the hallowed halls of Oxford University. For the bus driver's son, this represented the fulfilment of one of his great dreams.

None the less, Harry travelled to Oxford in a state of anxiety and trepidation. He made sure that he took with him his slides of oranges, bones, 'phantom' leaves and a variety of other Kirlian images with which many people in the field were by now somewhat familiar. The large auditorium was one of those where the chairs ascend away from the stage, seemingly rising onwards and outwards into infinity – at least when viewed from the perspective of the nervous young lecturer!

'Good morning, ladies and gentlemen,' began Harry, as he stood in front of the assembled throng of professors, PhDs and undergraduates. He moved on to show how the energy fields of breakfast cereals could be compared using Kirlian 'electronography' (by now called 'photography' by virtually everyone in the field). Organic or chemically unchanged muesli glowed and sparkled, while processed or chemically very changed breakfast cereal produced no recognizable energy pattern at all.

'As you can see, the sunshine breakfast seems to lack both sun and shine,' Harry commented, in what he thought was a funny quip. To his surprise, cries of 'Shame! shame!' rang out from all around the auditorium. 'De-bag him,' shouted one young student in the audience. Harry wondered what he'd said, but it seemed he would have little chance to find out because he was going to have difficulty getting another word in.

Then a grey-haired man in a long black gown rose slowly and sombrely in the front row and calmed the audience down.

'He asked me if I was aware that the very auditorium in which I was speaking had been built with a donation from a well-known company that made breakfast cereal!' Harry told us, smiling now at the thought of the chaos that he had unwittingly caused. 'Eventually they let me finish. But, as you can imagine, I was ready to duck any tomatoes or rotten eggs from that moment on.'

The next important development in Harry's life came through meeting Colonel Marcus McCausland, who was later to become a founder member of the Association for New Approaches to Cancer, which had a part in the development of the pioneering cancer research now being done in Bristol. His special interest was in natural health foods and, having heard about the Oldfield–Kirlian photographic techniques, he commissioned Harry to take a set of pictures of health foods. This commission helped enormously towards the further research funding which Harry needed to progress. The project involved examining the energetic differences between wholefoods and processed foods, and the results showed clear differences between the two. Subsequently, Colonel McCausland persuaded Harry to present his results to a meeting of the Health Education Council.

'The results received a good hearing and prompted much discussion,' said Harry. But there was more.

'At the end of the meeting, a young American biochemist working here in a London hospital asked permission to speak to me in private. As it turned out, he was working on the biochemical synthesis of cancer cells and tissues. His suggestion was that I should turn my attention away from nutrition and start looking at disease seriously rather than just dabbling, as I had been up to that time.

'His name was Glen Rein, and it was the beginning of a long and fruitful friendship.'

Not long afterwards, Harry arrived promptly at two in the afternoon at Dr Rein's laboratory. The two scientists soon became immersed in their work. 'The next thing I knew it was two in the morning,' remembers Harry.

Together, over the coming months, Harry and Glen Rein tested many kinds of tissue, exploring the use of Kirlian photography in a wide range of experiments. In some of these, Glen would act as the photographic subject. Harry often noticed something strange about his friend's Kirlian handprints: there would be times when he did not give out any energy for the Kirlian image to form.

Harry explains:

'There seemed no logical reason for this, nor was it connected with any ailments or changed mental states. Then the common denominator was finally uncovered: Glen used radioactive tracers occasionally in his normal work. Any time that he did so, his Kirlian energy level was drastically affected. This made both of us think seriously about what radiation of all kinds might be doing to human and animal energy fields, and those of plants and foodstuffs.'

Glen introduced Harry to a team of cancer researchers at a London hospital and together they assessed the potential usefulness of Harry's Kirlian camera in cancer detection.

This was confirmed by Dr Peter Kandela, a GP who had close links with the Royal Marsden Hospital, where he had once worked. 'I am satisfied that the technique shows up something in the body which is abnormal,' said Dr Kandela.

One experimental trial, in which five female patients with suspected cancer of the breast stood in a darkened room and held their outstretched fingers on a plastic sheet placed above a photographic Kirlian film, confirmed this. The luminous discharge produced by their fingertips after the high-energy field had been created for a minute or two was 'totally unlike that of healthy people'. Harry says:

'We initially examined human breast cancer biopsy specimens and compared them with normal adjacent tissue obtained at the same operation. The intensity of light emitted from the tumour tissues was substantially greater than that obtained from the normal tissue. It looked as if we had found something of true diagnostic interest.'

At that time there was a great deal of interest around the world in what Harry was doing with his Kirlian camera. For example, on 11 November 1980, *Esotera*, a magazine published in Germany, ran an article showing pictures of Harry and Glen and describing their work.

Harry was also creating quite a stir in medical research circles. The 13 September 1980 issue of *Pulse* (Vol.40, no.37), a medical publication in the form of a newspaper, featured his work on the front page: 'Kirlian photography is a novel way of photographing cell structure. Can it be used as a diagnostic tool'?

The article said: 'What is clear is that [Kirlian photographs] are recording a real event in some way associated with health and the disease process, and may be useful in a variety of diagnostic situations.'

Dr Roger Angold told *Pulse*: 'We are interested in aspects of seed performance – why some seed stock does better than others. If Kirlian photography can detect "subtle energies", it would be useful here as a diagnostic tool.' *Pulse* also suggested that GPs might use the machine for surgery diagnosis.

But despite the interest and successes, Harry was beginning to have his own doubts, especially concerning unwanted 'artefacts'.

He wanted to know whether he was measuring a real disturbance in the energy field or one caused by the process of measurement. Harry says of the mood at the time:

'The scientific community was increasingly asking whether Kirlian photography was some sort of Spiritualist mumbo jumbo or something of conventional scientific interest. Ever since the technique was first pioneered in the 1930s, before finally being brought to the West by two parapsychologists in 1950, it had generated much controversy. Common questions would arise: What makes the characteristic flare pattern? Can it be "read"? Can it be controlled?

'Some advocates claimed that Kirlian images can signify, for example, a person's creative abilities, his potential as a leader or his psychic energy. At the more conventional end of the spectrum, Russian nutrition experts had used Kirlian photographs to help them improve the quality of grain and other foodstuffs. Scientists at Rank-Hovis-MacDougall were using the process to study seed germination.

'Recent medical interest, given momentum by Dr Thelma Moss's experiments in America, had stimulated new theories about Kirlian photography's possible use in diagnosing cancer. It was reported that Dr Moss and her colleagues at the University of Rochester in New York had found a definite link between the intensity of the Kirlian image and cancer.

'The Kirlians themselves believed their device could detect illness but it wasn't until the 1960s, after Kirlian photography had been scrutinized by other scientists, that these claims were taken seriously. In the five years between 1975 and 1980, Kirlian photography had been subjected to considerable medical research, particularly in America and the East.'

In London, cancer specialists at the Royal Marsden and Charing Cross hospitals had investigated the technique as a possible mass screening instrument for tumours. Also, Dr Malcolm Carruthers, director of clinical studies at London's Maudsley Hospital, was using it for psychotherapy and as an aid in detecting disease. At the time he described the technique as 'an infant science with enormous potential as a diagnostic tool'.

Others, however, were less than convinced. They argued that there are too many uncontrollable factors. In the first place, they claimed that little is known about how the technique interacts with the body's chemistry or the salts secreted in our sweat. Furthermore, they questioned whether atmosphere, temperature or other factors influenced results. Dr Martin Walker, of the Joyce Green Hospital in Kent, for example, was concerned about the chemical reactions which take place between the skin and photographic paper.

The exact nature of the Kirlian phenomenon had also been baffling many scientists. Some claimed it was no more than a discharge of ions, not an inexplicable force.

Harry overcame this objection by introducing a completely new and clean electrode for the 'phantom' image, so that no water or other material from the subject could influence the 'phantom effect'. He thus proved that the effect was still producible on the clean electrode which could not have any residual artefacts from the first picture electrode.

Nevertheless, others were voicing what Harry considered to be valid doubts. One such critic was Arthur Ellison, a professor of electronics and electrical engineering at City University in London and a former president of the Society for Psychical Research. Harry met Professor Ellison at Oxford University when both were presenting papers on psychical research and phenomena for the Department of External Studies. He was very impressed:

'Professor Ellison was precise, logical and open minded and I found him to be well-informed on both the scientific and psychical side of things and a very balanced and fair man. I welcomed his constructive criticisms at that time because they helped point me in the right direction for some of the things I did later on.'

Professor Ellison outlined the importance of looking at variables in general – such as the temperature, humidity of the air, voltage, waveform, the duration of the discharge with its frequency, and the consistency of the film. Another critic of the Kirlian technique, Professor Yoshiaki Omura of the International Kirlian Research Association, went somewhat further and identified 24 specific variables that should be controlled in any Kirlian experiment.

Harry believed there was merit in these comments and took them on board in his further Kirlian research. He remained committed to finding a method of unveiling the invisible energy template which he believed directed the form of physical objects, so that he could devise a technique with which to scan for disease.

Harry had introduced the idea of disease detection to his school science club. During the many experiments they carried out, he began to notice that subjects being photographed with the Kirlian camera were also transmitting 'signals' when they were in contact with the device.

The signals seemed to vary according to the number of pulses that were induced into the subject. Harry had originally started with one pulse and then went on to experiment with a range of pulses.

The discovery that the body could be made to emit signals opened up the possibility of whole body scanning, as opposed to hand scanning, and was a very important step towards achieving readings in three dimensions.

First Harry increased the voltage which was induced through the subject:

'I stepped up the voltage and invented three-dimensional Kirlian photography. First of all, I was interested in making things very visual and I developed my own transparent electrodes, so you could see through the energies.

'I knew that the hypothetical energy field had to be 3-D, so I wanted a way of casting the field effect around a 3-D object and this I did with a home-made version of a Faraday cage or screen. I constructed a mesh dome around the object and created the field within this spherical form with the object on a pedestal inside. Earthing was through the pedestral.

'Later on, I tried doing this with human volunteers on huge Tesla coils which I had borrowed. But we had to stop after a couple of hours because the sensation was so disconcerting to the person being photographed. The problem was that it was like being plunged into an ants' nest with biting ants crawling all over you. I know this becasue I tried it myself first to ensure the safety.

'This was definitely an unwanted artefact which made it impossible to discern whether or not we were seeing a natural energetic effect or something generated by the stimulation of the field.

'Another problem was that the method we were using could knock out the television screen about five or six doors down from where we were working. We produced radio interference, television interference – you name it, we interfered with it. And it was a no-go area as far as the GPO were concerned, if you get my drift. So we caused a few problems with that particular method.'

Undaunted, Harry tried lowering the voltage and upping the frequency, with the result that the visual or light image was lost but the body reacted by emitting signals in the radio and sound ranges. These could be measured with a probe connected to an oscilloscope, which provided an instant 'picture' of the invisible energies around the subject. Harry called this probe the 'Kirlian gun' because the barrel made it look like one. Very soon afterwards he was proving that he could diagnose disease with it.

Harry's work began attracting the attention of the local media. In June 1980, the *West London Observer* carried an article entitled 'The Cancer Detectives', which began by telling the story of the scanner Harry and Ian and the school science club children had made. Harry commented about the work his 'team' had been doing in 3-D cancer detection:

> 'Together with Mr McGibbon and a doctor, Peter Kandela, we have been developing the device. We have been working on it for over a year, mainly in our spare time, like after school. Some nights, though, we have stayed up to the early hours of the morning with our research ...
>
> 'As cancerous tumours give off higher and stronger frequencies than healthy, normal tissue, it is possible to detect them.'

Harry's PIP scanner now highlights this phenomenon on a regular basis (a PIP image of a man with a bladder tumour can be seen in the plate section). Harry says:

> 'Cancer can be thought of as a rapid division of "rogue" cells which the body's police force, the immune system, is unable to control. The over-activity of the cells would be expected to cause a corresponding convex "bump" in the energy field at or near the site of the tumour. You will notice from the bladder tumour PIP image side view that this is exactly what appears to be happening. You will also notice the red lines of congestion in the energy field all down the front of the man's body.
>
> 'Electro-crystal therapy seeks to quieten the "rebellion" and restore order and calm. When order is restored, another PIP image would hopefully provide evidence of this to the concerned patient.'

Harry has found that being able to show before and after PIP images is of great comfort to those who seek his help. But this is how Harry's work stands today. To continue with the story we must return to 1980.

Harry's early tests involving the Kirlian gun had been very encouraging and Peter Begent, senior lecturer in medical oncology at Charing Cross Hospital, had been sufficiently interested to ask for more information on the machine. Harry was also gaining a fair amount of press coverage, including a lead article in the January 1981 issue of *BMA News Review*, a journal produced by the British Medical Association and sent monthly to all doctors working in the United Kingdom. This prestigious journal described Kirlian photography as 'a diagnostic tool which may offer something to conventional medicine'.

Further national coverage came in the *Guardian* of 22 January, 1981, under the heading 'A shot to the heart'. Here a journalist who had watched one of Harry's demonstrations of the Kirlian gun described his experience:

'The Kirlian gun might or might not reveal the aura of the human soul. But it does seem to yield diagnostic results.

'A medical researcher aims a strange pistol-shaped device with a nine-inch barrel at the chest of a fully dressed middle-aged man at London's Charing Cross Hospital. Then he fires!

'The gun makes no sound but the man's heart reacts instantly. It starts to beam out radio distress signals which appear as spiky green graph peaks on an oscilloscope display similar to a television screen.

'Within 60 seconds the operator, Mr Harry Oldfield, a biologist, tells the man ... "You have a heart abnormality."

'A young nutritionist from New Zealand is next to move into the gun's sights at the demonstration. Oldfield points the device at various points of her body briefly. "You appear to have an abdominal problem," he says with deliberate vagueness as he interprets her body's returning signals on the glowing screen. Afterwards she discretely admits that her doctor has diagnosed a blocked Fallopian tube.

'It was a remarkable display of a curious development known as Kirlian Electrography ... Some British medical researchers who have used Kirlian devices say that they work on the principle that the human body possesses hitherto unidentified and uncharted energy forces.

'This energy can be stimulated by the Kirlian gun which focuses high-energy, high-frequency radio signals into a patient's body to induce what is termed "harmonic resonance" from the tissues themselves. The patient then responds with silent radio signals of a special kind if disease is present.'

Since the term 'harmonic resonance' is used frequently to describe certain aspects of Harry's work we asked him to explain it in simple terms. He said:

'Perhaps the best example is a tuning fork. If you strike a tuning fork it will vibrate at a certain note (or frequency). A string of the same note on a piano will start to vibrate in "harmonious resonance", although the two are not physically touching.

'I believe the same was happening in the human body when we used the Kirlian gun. The equipment was like the tuning fork and the human body vibrated in harmonic resonance just like the string. It is also important to mention that, in the human example, we are talking about this happening on much finer scales.'

The Kirlian gun was for Harry the culmination of his long search for an energy field scanner which could be used to diagnose areas of possible physical abnormality in three dimensions by obtaining quantitative measurements from all around the body. The previous Kirlian results had been in two dimensions; the Kirlian gun added 'depth of field', as Harry calls it, and could be used in real time without the need for darkroom conditions. This represented a giant leap forward in terms of practical application in a clinical setting.

At the end of 1981, Harry explained these ideas to *Medical News Weekly* (17–24 December 1981):

'It appears we all have our own specific resonant frequency and the input must match, and harmonize, with this. If the energy source is connected to the subject and tuned to the specific individual, the subject effectively becomes a radio beacon ...

'One can detect this radio or ultrasound emission with the aid of an appropriate detector, and can display what is picked up on an oscilloscope. It appears that certain wave forms (as seen on the oscilloscope) and certain frequencies may be diagnostic. There appears to be more sound from places where there are rapidly dividing cells.'

Later, Harry came up with the idea of using 'triangulation', which enabled him to measure the depth of a tumour inside the body by taking readings at a number of positions and working out the location of the tumour by comparing them.

This was not all. As Harry also explained:

'The scanning technique also shows non-specific changes in the discharge over any part of the body where there is, or has been, some abnormality, such as old fractures, areas of inflammation and muscle tension for example.'

To explain exactly how this could come about, Harry told us something more about electromagnetism, resonance and fields:

'To tell the whole story, credit must be given to the early pioneers in the investigation into invisible energies.

'It was during the 1860s that James Clerk Maxwell's unified theory of electromagnetism enabled electricity, magnetism and light to be brought within a broad mathematical framework. Physics could now be expanded, but also radically changed because Maxwell's theory placed in the heart of physics the concept of *fields*. But what exactly are fields?

'Since they behave like waves but do not appear to need a physical medium like air in which to travel, Maxwell thought that fields were modifications of a subtle medium, the aether. Later it was discovered that electromagnetic energies had a strange property: they did not appear to need any medium through which to travel.

'An *electric field* forms around any electric charge. This means that any other charged object will be attracted – if the polarities are opposite – or repelled – if they are the same – for a certain distance around a first object. The field is the region of space in which an electrical charge can be detected and it is measured in volts per unit of area.

'Electric fields must be distinguished from *magnetic fields*. Like charge, magnetism is a dimly understood intrinsic property of matter that manifests in two polarities. However, we do know that electric and magnetic fields appear to travel in three dimensions, like rippling waves, at 90 degrees to each other. This means they can exert a *force*. But unlike sound energy, which moves and exerts a force through a physical medium like air by causing pressure waves, it was found that field energy does not need a physical medium in which to exert itself.

'Any flow of electrons sets up a combined electric and magnetic field around the current, which in turn affects other electrons nearby. Around a direct current the *electromagnetic field* is stable, whereas an alternating current's field collapses and reappears with its poles reversed with every voltage cycle. This reversal happens perhaps 40, 50 or 60 times a second in our normal house electricity supplies, depending on the system used in each country. Just as an electric current produces a magnetic field, when a conductor is moved through a magnetic field a current is induced in it.

'In 1888, a German physicist called Heinrich Hertz made the first experimental discovery of radio waves. The vibratory rate of electromagnetic radiation was named after him – the Hertz or cycle per second. The Hertz value indicates the frequency of wave motion.

'For the purpose of explanation we could use a simple analogy. If two people hold the ends of a rope and one of them moves their end of the rope up and down, a "wave" will travel down the rope. If the wave-generating person uses more power by moving the rope up and down faster, then the frequency of the waves will increase – there will be more complete cycles going down the rope in the same time and this will generally mean a more powerful force is exerted by the radiation.

'So, both electric and magnetic fields are really just abstractions that scientists have made up to try to understand electricity's and magnetism's action at a distance, produced by no known intervening material or energy, a phenomenon we now call "electromagnetic resonance" but which used to be considered impossible.

'A field is represented by lines of force, another abstraction, to indicate its direction and shape. Both kinds of fields weaken with distance (attenuate), but their influence is technically infinite. Imagine this: field theory suggests that every time you use your toaster, the fields around it perturb charged particles in the farthest galaxies, albeit ever so slightly and millions of years later.

'There is a whole universe full of unseen electromagnetic energy. This is a sea of radiation that the current consensus in orthodox science believes to be both waves in electromagnetic fields and particles at the same time. I find this hard to accept and am looking for other ways of explaining what is observed.

'This sea of invisible electromagnetic radiation includes cosmic rays, gamma rays, X-rays and radio waves. A small part of the spectrum is visible, of course, and this is what we generally mean when we use the word "light".

'Electromagnetic fields interact in many complex ways that have given rise to much of the natural world that we experience with our senses. I thought that the fields produced by the body might indicate things that are going on in the physical cells and wanted a way to measure what was happening to them. Over time, I gradually learned that the measurements also gave me information about the mental and emotional state of the person. It seemed as if the physical was linked to these other aspects. This was fascinating. I thought that here we may have a way of measuring why stress might go on to cause cancer, for example.

'Physicists have been trying for generations to solve the fundamental mysteries of electromagnetism and few have succeeded to their own satisfaction. One man who came closer than most was Nikola Tesla, whom I regard very highly. I was magnetically attracted to Tesla's ideas very early in my career and a Tesla coil is used in my electro-generators.'

Harry went on to tell us some more about Tesla and his work:

'Tesla was a physicist and electrical engineer who invented fluorescent lighting, the Tesla induction motor and the Tesla coil. He also developed the alternating current (AC) electrical supply system.

'He was very interested in the possibility of radio communication and as early as 1897 he demonstrated remote control of two model boats on a pond. In 1900 he began to construct a broadcasting station on Long Island, New York, in the hope of developing "World Wireless", but lost his funding. He also outlined a scheme for detecting ships at sea, which was later developed as radar. One of his most ambitious ideas was to transmit electricity to anywhere in the world without wires by using the Earth itself as an enormous oscillator. In his later years, Tesla spent his time on various unusual projects, like the invention of devices for photographing thoughts on the retina of the eye.

'The Tesla coil is an air core transformer with the primary and secondary windings tuned in resonance to produce high-frequency, high-voltage electricity. Using this device, Tesla produced an electric spark 135 feet long in 1899. He

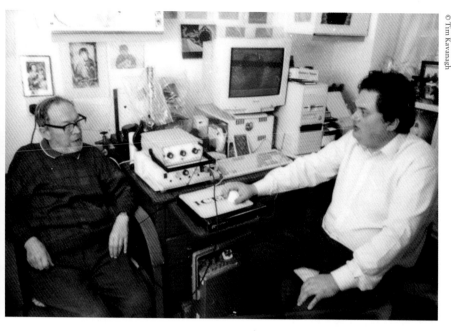

Above: Harry carries out a consultation and treatment session with a patient in his office.

Below: On the left is a Kirlian image of a frozen orange. Compare its corona with that of the orange on the right, which has not been frozen. Harry carried out a wide range of tests on foods with his early Kirlian equipment. His work stimulated interest from a number of groups, including the Health Education Council.

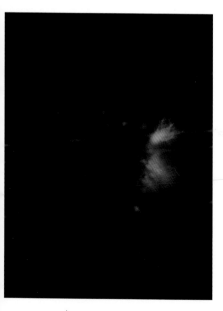
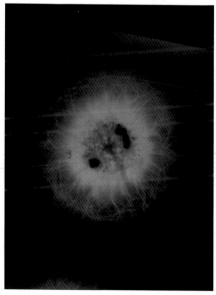

Above: Harry is holding Big Bertha, a giant electrode filled with citrine and clear quartz crystals in saline. Amongst other things, Harry has used Big Bertha for his weather experiments in Iceland.
Above: Singer Björk regularly uses electro-crystal therapy. She has her own electro-crystal generator.

Below: The seven colours or healing rays used in electro-crystal therapy are represented here by the seven vertical crystal-filled silicone tubes. One of the ringed tubes is filled with rose quartz, which is effective on the whole energy field. The other ringed tube is called the 'universal' electrode as it contains crystals of all seven rays. This is the standard issue silicone electrode.
Below: Here the four versions of the electro-crystal generator can be seen stacked in order with the oldest at the top and the newest at the bottom. These devices generate the high-frequency electromagnetic pulses which 'excite' the crystals.

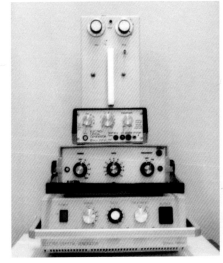

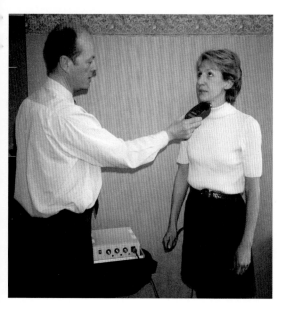

Left: Here a patient is being scanned with the electro-scanning method, or ESM. Harmless sound and radio signals from the electro-crystal generator are induced into the body via the crystal and saline electrode, which is held in the hand. The returning signals are detected with a hand-held scanner to provide diagnostic information about the energy field.

Below: This person has a bladder tumour. Polycontrast interference photography or PIP images often show a bulge in the energy field in the area of a malignant tumour. In this case a bulge can be seen to start in the energy field at the level of the bladder. An ESM reading will normally detect a surplus of energy in the same area as the bulge seen on the PIP scan, thus providing a quantitative confirmation of the qualitative information provided by PIP.

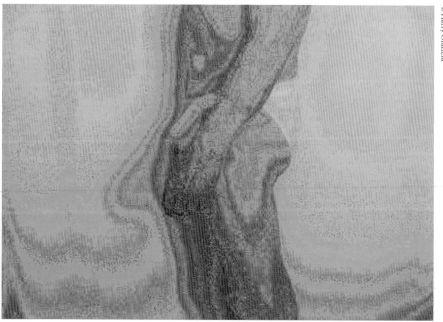

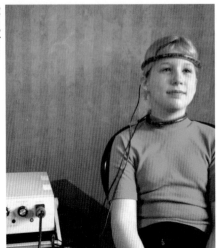

Above: Young Kimberley is having a treatment for a sore throat and congested sinuses. One flexible silicone tube, containing amethyst crystals, is placed on the brow. Another, containing sodalite crystals, is placed around the throat.

Above: One therapist was amazed when this injured bird visited the garden daily to sit on the active crystal electrode (which had been left on the lawn by accident). The bird was initially unable to fly. After a few days of self-administered 'treatment', it flew away.

Below: Ex-naval officer John Arber regularly attends Harry's clinic for electro-crystal and opto-crystal therapy. John, seen here being treated with the eye-visor, reports that his optician has been very surprised at the improvement in his eyesight.

Below: Mark Lester is an electro-crystal therapist who regularly uses electro-crystal therapy to 'maintain health and well-being'. Here we can see him using a number of devices, including the opto-crystal therapy blue-light and aquamarine accessory.

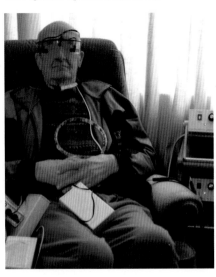

also lit more than 200 lamps over a distance of 25 miles without the use of intervening wires. Gas-filled tubes are readily energized by high-frequency currents and so lights of this type were easily operated within the field of a large Tesla coil. Tesla soon developed all manner of coils which have since found numerous applications in electrical and electronic devices, including our electro-crystal generator.

'Some of Tesla's work was somewhat controversial. Governments appear to have long been concerned about the potential for tuned and amplified resonating devices to destroy structures and people just as easily as they might organize structures and heal people.

'Tesla not only used the principle of electromagnetic resonance to light his laboratory with wireless light bulbs, but also carried out experiments with mechanical oscillators. He would screw the base of one of his small mechanical oscillators to an iron supporting pillar in the middle of his laboratory and set it into oscillation. He had noticed that it took some time to build up its maximum speed of vibration and the longer it operated, the faster the tempo it attained.

'During the experiments, the many objects around the laboratory would suddenly go into violent vibration as they came into resonance with the fundamental vibration of the oscillator or some harmonic of it. But Tesla had noticed that not all the objects responded in the same way to the vibrations. As the output from the oscillator changed, one object would stop vibrating and some other object, in resonance with the new rate, would start.

'At the police headquarters down the road they had become quite familiar with the strange sounds and lights coming from the Tesla laboratory. But one particular morning the police were surprised to feel the building rumbling under their feet and find chairs moving across floors with no one near them. They rushed to the Tesla building and ran up the stairs – and as they did so they felt the building vibrating even more strongly. Just as they rushed into

Tesla's laboratory to tackle whatever it was that was causing the chaos, the vibrations stopped.

'On entering the room, the police witnessed a strange sight. They were just in time to see the tall and lanky figure of the inventor swing a heavy sledgehammer to shatter a small iron contraption mounted on the post in the middle of the room. The rumbling chaos gave way to a deep heavy silence.

'So you can probably now understand the potential power of electromagnetic resonance for both good and ill.

'The day after Tesla died in January 1943, the FBI removed all his research papers. It is thought that his ideas were used by the government, after his death, for the electromagnetic resonance trial, known as the Philadelphia Experiment, in October 1943.'

This experiment, in which a US Navy ship was seen to disappear and reappear during a top-secret electromagnetic resonance test of some kind, with horrendous ramifications for the crew, is a story so well documented that there is very likely something in it that scared the government considerably.

Harry is, of course, only interested in using electromagnetic resonance in helping and healing, in normalizing and balancing, rather than harming and destroying. On this point, Otto Rahn, a well-known bacteriologist, had this to say in 1946 to an inventor, T. Galen Hieronymus, who had asked for advice:

'Since those radiations hold the secret of life, they also hold the secret of death. At present very few people know about the possibilities, and very few know all the facts. It seems imperative that those few keep their knowledge to themselves, and divulge only as much as necessary to perform the immediate applications to cure disease. Your discoveries open up great possibilities, as tremendous as those of the atom bomb, and just like atomic energy, these radiations may be used for the bad as well as the good of humanity.'

We asked Harry what had so alarmed Otto Rahn. He replied:

'Hieronymus had isolated three ears of corn and on each one placed a corn worm. He then began to treat them with his radionic broadcaster, a machine for which he obtained a patent (number 2,482,773) in 1949 in the United States and others subsequently in the United Kingdom and Canada.

'After three days of continuous treatment at the rate of 10 minutes per hour, two of the corn worms had been reduced to just "wet places" on the corn ears and the third was a shapeless mass. Not unnaturally, Hieronymus was shocked by the lethal potential of tuned radiation.

'Trying to describe the radiation he had unearthed, he speculated that a certain energy, obeying some of the laws of electricity but not all of them and some of the laws of optics but not all of them, does indeed exist and he called it "eloptic energy".'

Others have found evidence of such an energy and have used various words to try to describe it. However, Harry Oldfield appears to be the first to systematically unveil this elusive energy.

Harry continued with his explanation of some of the uses to which these energies may have been put:

'Dr Robert Beck says he left the employ of the American government because what he was doing began to challenge his ethics. He says he was able to sit in a restaurant and raise or lower the level of conversation in the room by adjusting an electromagnetic transmitter built into his wrist-watch.

'And before you conclude that this is probably science fiction, consider that Dr Beck is a widely respected authority in his field, not some nutty professor type.

'Then there is the case of what the Western secret services learned to call "the Woodpecker". If you completely lower the aerial on a radio, even local radio broadcasts are very hard to pick up. If, however, during the Cold War, you tuned in to the Soviet Woodpecker frequency band, the tap, tap, tap of 10 pulses per second they had been beaming at the West for decades came through loud and clear.

'We might reasonably ask why the Soviet Union decided to spend billions of roubles placing powerful transmitters all along their border with the West. Why did they pulse 10 Hertz or cycles per second at us all day long for so many years? The answer to this has not yet emerged, even though the Iron Curtain came down some time ago.'

One idea is that, since 10 Hz is the alpha rhythm or the measured 'meditation state' of the brain, the Soviets were trying to passify the 'imperialist aggressors'. Interestingly, cats, our soothing household companions, also purr in alpha rhythm frequencies! Less well known is operation Grill Flame, which involves 'remote viewing'. This is the practice of tuning in to people and events – say, a secret military base – without actually being physically present. Various US army personnel, some of very senior rank, are now coming forward with details on their role in specialist remote viewing espionage units and a television programme shown during 1997 suggested that remote viewing is being increasingly used by the military.

The 'viewer' is normally a soldier who has high security clearance and has or develops a recognizable psychic ability. Often this occurs after a head injury. The confused soldier reports to the medical officer with 'visions' or other experiences, expecting to be relieved of duty for a while, but instead is whisked off to a hut in the middle of a forest for new training.

Here these soldiers learn to sit in a room and 'see' what's going on behind enemy lines. So, it seems that whilst governments appear to sanction the ridicule of 'psychic' or 'paranormal' research and practice, their special forces might be engaged in non-stop 'psychic spying'.

Further to the possible concern of the authorities about these extraordinary energies, Harry and Roger Coghill note in their book that the pioneers of research into life energies appear to have been singled out and systematically ostracized, hounded and humiliated into silence or even suicide. Why?

For now, Harry continues with the history of the medical application of electromagnetism:

'In 1895, Wilhelm Roentgen discovered X-rays. But the first scientist to devote most of his research career to studying life, health and disease from the point of view of electromagnetism was Georges Lakhovsky. Shortly after the First World War he developed the theory that all life on Earth is a phenomenon created and maintained by electromagnetic radiation, chiefly that which occurs in cosmic rays. Most of this radiation originates beyond the solar system and blends with that from the sun to bombard the Earth.

'Lakhovsky asserted that when the sunspot cycle is at its peak the incidence of heart complaints and other diseases rises. He thought this was due to the solar activity interfering with the influx of cosmic radiation from beyond the solar system.

'It is now known that, when sunspots are at their peak, the 'solar wind' of particles from the sun increases in intensity and alters the composition of the cosmic radiation reaching the Earth. This, Lakhovsky would say, also alters the nature of the invisible sea of energy through which we all swim.

'Lakhovsky said that disease is "a war of radiations" and the battleground is the basic component of all living things – the cell. He believed that the cell is actually an electrical circuit which both receives and emits radiation. One has only to upset the balance of this oscillation and disease will result.

'In 1931 Lakhovsky brought out his multiple wave oscillator (MWO), a device that generated electromagnetic waves with frequencies ranging from the extremely low all the way up to those of visible light. By bombarding the body with all the frequencies at once he hoped that the diseased area would absorb the appropriate one.'

Harry's techniques, by comparison, are much more sophisticated and finely tuned, targeting specific 'windows' of frequency to enable the human energy system to balance itself and harmonize with its environment.

Harry continued his history:

'Lakhovsky and other independent researchers published details of several cases, complete with before and after photographs, in which the MWO had been used to treat a variety of skin ulcers, radium burns and tumours, presumably because results would be easy to see.

'One of the most remarkable cases was that of an 82-year-old woman who had been hideously disfigured by an epithelioma [cancer of the body's surface tissue] on her cheek that was almost as big as her ear. It had resisted radium therapy [a radioactive burning substance used by modern medicine which in fact made it worse] but completely disappeared after three weeks of MWO treatment, leaving the woman with a smooth cheek and looking years younger.

'The before and after pictures showed how remarkable the improvements can be with this type of treatment.

'Lakhovsky also revived the nineteenth-century fashion for wearing copper belts and bracelets, which he regarded as miniature MWOs. In a well documented experiment at the Salpêtrière Hospital in Paris, he inoculated six geraniums with tumour-forming bacteria and placed a single turn of copper wire around one of them. Five of the plants were dead within a fortnight, but the one that had been encircled with the copper thrived and grew to an enormous height – and the tumour eventually withered and fell off.'

Today, Harry uses water 'energized' with his electro-crystal generator to grow huge tomatoes and other plants. A gardener's dream come true?

It is beyond the scope of this book to go into any more historical detail, but it is clear that investigations into the extraordinary energies from the invisible universe have been interesting scientists, governments and others for some time.

To return to Harry's explorations, at the time of the *Medical News Weekly* article in December 1981 no formal trials of the Kirlian gun had taken place, though Harry had performed some preliminary experiments with Dr Andrew Lockie, a GP and practitioner of acupuncture and homoeopathy in West Ealing, London.

Harry had scanned 10 patients 'blind' with Dr Lockie observing. 'We took a read-out on the state of the organs,' said the doctor. 'Degenerative diseases appear to deplete the field, whereas inflammation produces an increase. The Kirlian gun might be valuable as an early warning device, providing a method of non-specific scanning which can be followed up.'

Harry explains this further with another of his simple analogies:

'This field can be imagined as an "electric atmosphere", a human weather system in which an invisible wind blows over the surface of the skin. Where physical tissues were under-functioning (e.g. MS), they would "suck" the wind in, causing a concave dent in the field and a lower than normal reading would be obtained in the area of the problem.

'I observed that where physical tissues were over-functioning (e.g. cancer), they would produce a "gust" in the wind, with storm-like turbulence in the presence of rapidly dividing cancer cells, causing a convex bump in the field and a higher than normal reading would be obtained in the area of the problem.

'To continue with this human weather system analogy, there could also be what we might call whirlwinds, ozone leaks, jet streams, clouds and even lightning in this body atmosphere.'

Some claimed that these effects were evidence of the 'mitogenic ray' postulated by the German biophysicist F. A. Popp, who demonstrated that a healthy onion seedling has a beneficial effect on the growth of a less healthy one when it is placed nearby. This effect can be prevented by a glass screen placed between the onions, but not by a quartz one, implying some form of ultraviolet radiation passing between the two. Popp suggested that 'rays' are emitted from a cell that control the division of others and that this 'mitogenic ray emission' may be out of control in cancer.

Whatever the principles behind the Kirlian gun, as *Medical News Weekly* commented, 'It would be a pity if the whole idea is rejected out of hand because it is employing some phenomenon we cannot yet explain.'

However, even at the time, many scientists were intrigued by Harry's ideas. Harry, Ian and their team of children were invited to demonstrate the Kirlian gun at a Royal Society of Medicine cancer conference and the machines were soon being used in laboratories, clinics and hospitals elsewhere in Britain, including Charing Cross Hospital, just down the road from the school. Among the other hospitals where doctors began expressing interest in the technique were the Maudsley Hospital, London, and Joyce Green Hospital, Dartford, Kent. Many of those who saw the device in action agreed that it was a very valuable potential early warning system for detecting cancer.

The Maudsley Hospital's Dr Malcolm Carruthers, who had made a close study of the Kirlian phenomenon, told a cancer meeting at Charing Cross:

'The technique is comparable to early X-ray techniques before hospitals were equipped with instruments such as computerized tomography X-rays. Human beings are both radiators and receivers of many different subtle forms of energy, some of which we can detect and some of which, so far, we have been unable to capture on instruments.'

Because of the success of his research, Harry was spending almost all of his spare time on his invention and was considering quitting his job to develop it further.

By now he had introduced an ordinary sound level meter with which he could 'listen' to the signals coming from the body. This did away with the need for the Kirlian gun and oscilloscope contraption, which was a little unwieldy for demonstrations and practical clinical purposes. Harry's electro-generator produced the signals from the body and he could see the needle move on the sound meter, which gave him a plus or minus reading when compared with the person's 'zero balance', or relatively normal reading. This enabled him to ascertain whether a particular area of the body was over or under-energetic relative to the norm for that person.

Harry had developed great skill at putting all this information together to arrive at a very comprehensive overall diagnosis of a person's state of health – and all in a few minutes. He called his new idea the 'electro-scanning method', or ESM.

Harry had now proved to his own satisfaction that his new way of diagnosis worked, and he had been giving demonstrations at public and private gatherings all over Britain. With such interest being generated at home, it is not surprising that he was invited to America to show other researchers his progress. Late in 1983, he travelled to San Francisco.

Still only 30 years old, the young scientist was understandably nervous as he faced a packed house comprising 200 doctors, scientists, researchers and interested members of the public. He began as usual: 'Could I please have a number of volunteers for scanning? I would like you to come up one at a time. The only proviso is that I must never have met the people who come up to be scanned.'

At his demonstrations Harry often astounds audiences with the breadth and depth of knowledge he appears to have about an individual he has only just met. 'Does he get it psychically?' is a question often asked, while at the other end of the scale of responses comes the comment: 'He must be wired!' This was the reaction of one of the doctors in the San Francisco audience. 'Hold everything!' he shouted, jumping up from his seat at the front of the auditorium and motioning to a security guard to approach the stage. In what was obviously a pre-planned operation, he literally raced up the steps and across the stage to where Harry was standing. Grabbing the microphone, he asked in an accusing tone: 'Do we have permission to frisk you, Mr Oldfield?'

When in San Francisco ... Harry thought, smiling inwardly to himself. 'By all means,' he replied in his usual obliging manner.

The security guard was instructed to search Harry from top to bottom and back to front.

'Nope. He's clean,' he reported, to the obvious disappointment of Harry's accuser.

'Have you checked behind his ears?'

Harry told us that he wasn't worried – he'd had a shower that morning!

'Yep, and he's clean as a whistle,' came the reply.

It later transpired that the doctor was a member of a group of Californian doctors and scientists who call themselves 'the Quackbusters'. This group spends a lot of time 'hunting down charlatans and quacks who operate in sects and other quasi-religious front organizations'. I suppose their interruption could be seen as a compliment to Harry's impressive scanning results, but viewed in another way, it was perhaps a little impolite!

By now Harry was becoming more and more convinced that electro 'patterns' of some kind may direct the course of disease and may be detectable before they produce their biological effects. He began to gather evidence that ESM could locate *potential* disorders.

This new form of diagnosis was extremely significant. A major problem with illness is that in many cases the doctor finds it as difficult to diagnose a disease as to cure it, and for a potentially serious illness, the earliest possible advance warning is essential. To be able to diagnose a disease before its malign effects appear is every clinician's dream. Dr Carruthers, who had watched Harry demonstrate the ESM a number of times, said at the time:

'It is possible that it may pick up disturbances of the body's bioplasmic field, the hypothetical field associated with living matter, that precede disease. This is unproven, but it is definitely interesting and worth pursuing...'

The 'hypothetical bioplasmic field' to which Dr Carruthers referred was, for Harry, the very essence of his work. Earlier researchers, like Professor Harold Saxton Burr, Dr Robert Becker and the more contemporary Dr Rupert Sheldrake, had used various terms for the phenomenon – such as bioelectricity, L-fields, body electricity, organizing fields of life, morphic resonance and so on – but they were all referring to the general concept of morphogenetic fields.

However, Harry began to prefer the term 'radiated morphogenetic field', as this best describes what the energy field phenomenon means to him. 'Morphogenetic field' means the origin of form, the organizing blueprint, the electronic *Doppelgänger*, the double, the design behind the structure. But 'radiated morphogenetic field' means something else as well: a field which is constantly referencing with the brain of the organism in question.

Later Harry proposed that this idea could be taken even further. The brain is not only constantly transceiving information in this space-time continuum so that a human being can function normally on a day-to-day level, but it is also a quantum mechanical device which is constantly communicating with other realms of reality. Information from these other realms of the invisible universe is assimilated and mixed by our brains with the survival information necessary for Earth functioning in each space-time moment. All of this adds up to a level of consciousness and an experience of life which is 'more than the sum of what we think are the parts'.

Eventually Harry left his teaching job to undertake cancer diagnosis and other research with the hospitals full time. At first this joint research went well, but after a little while Harry began to realize to his dismay that some standard hospital treatments might also weaken the body's natural defences and even hamper recovery. When he began voicing his concerns he very quickly ceased to be the golden boy and was asked to disassociate himself from the hospitals.

Harry initially thought this was a set-back but soon realized that it might be an opportunity to take his work a stage further. He had noticed, when he was diagnosing people with ESM, that they had reported feeling better after being in contact with his electro-generating machine. This had set him thinking, but he had not done any real research into it. But now, left with little alternative by his sudden departure from the hospital research programme, he decided to try to find whether it was the case that the electro-generator or a similar instrument could be used to heal people as well. He was excited by the possibility that he might be able to invent healing instruments as this would represent a full circle back to his original dream: healing people.

Filled with enthusiasm, Harry began experimenting with offering people treatment after their diagnosis. He knew that his electro-generator was a kind of radio-wave spray gun that, in a very subtle and harmless way, 'excites' every cell in the body so that they each vibrate a little and can thus be measured with an appropriate meter to see if they are giving off healthy signals. To his amazement, he soon discovered that by exciting the energy field and the cells with 'controlled vibrations' he could put unhealthy cells back into their normal healthy state of vibration. It appeared that his electro-generator really did have treatment potential.

However, Harry scrupulously avoided making specific claims for his technique. 'It is still at an embryonic stage,' he insisted, 'and it is a complementary therapy, not an alternative to conventional medicine.' This is still true, but today Harry can point to thousands upon thousands of cases where people appear to have benefited from his techniques and therapies. In the light of his own evidence, Harry has become increasingly confident. For the last two decades he has openly invited a scientific, double-blind, placebo-controlled study of his work.

A very important part of Harry's work with ESM therapy involved the development of a suitable electrode. An electrode is, he explained, 'a device, usually metal, that connects electronic equipment to a living organism for the purpose of measuring electric currents or voltages in the organism, or delivering a measured electrical stimulus to the organism'. Harry had tried metal electrodes but soon moved on to glass test tubes filled with salt water: an electrolyte ('any chemical compound that, when dissolved, for example in water, separates into charged atoms (ions) or molecules that conduct an electric current through the solution'). Harry explains:

> 'The salt crystal molecules are made up of sodium and chlorine atoms. When the salt crystals are dissolved, the salt dissociates into positively charged sodium and negatively charged chlorine ions and so enables electricity to flow. We used physiological saline, a 0.9 per cent solution, which is the same concentration as the fluids in the body and can be acquired easily from any chemist's shop.'

The electrolyte solution in the test tube would transfer the energy Harry had produced with his electro-generator to the subject (normally a person) and then to ground by what is known as a secondary induced field effect. Harry often calls this effect 'induction' or 'charging without touching'. He achieved some very encouraging results with the instrument. But the real breakthrough came when he was given the idea of using crystals.

CRYSTAL

'Nature has never made two human beings, two plants or two crystals exactly alike. Consider the magnitude of that diversity.'

THE BOOK OF THE SACRED STONES

I N the early '80s Harry met Mrs Anne Warren-Davies, a medical herbalist, whom he credits with giving him the idea of looking at crystals with Kirlian photography:

'When I first discovered, by accident, that the electro-generator component of ESM could also be used as a therapy, I wanted to offer this to people. I began sharing a clinic with Anne in Battersea and one day, out the blue, she mentioned that crystals might be worth a look at with my Kirlian equipment. And from that chance suggestion a whole new therapy emerged.'

Harry had expected the inorganic or 'dead' crystals to give off very little energy. But three years of experiments soon showed him that this was very far from the case.

The first thing Harry confirmed was that crystals amplify energy:

'They also transduce energy, which means that they change one type of energy into another. If you stimulate them with electricity you produce mechanical energy and they vibrate. And, when you stimulate them mechanically, say, with a hammer, you produce electrical energy. This is called the "piezoelectric" property of crystals. *Piezo* means "to press" or "to strike" in Greek.

'From there, I decided to do some more experiments with crystals.'

The first question to be asked and answered was: 'What exactly *is* a crystal?'

Harry explains:

'The word "crystal" originates from the Greek word for ice: *crystallos*. Our ancestors are thought to have seen crystals as "frozen water" from heaven or "solidified light". In modern understanding a crystal is a solid material in which the atoms are arranged in a regular pattern.

'Some crystals are described as "liquid crystals" and these are now thought by some scientists to be the basic structure of brain fluids; and of course liquid crystals are used in portable computer screens and other digital interfaces.

'Crystals form, or crystallize, from either the molten state or from solution. They are best defined as "structures" rather than "things" and are classified in a number of ways including their "habits" and "systems".

'A mineral is classically defined as an inorganic (not carbon-based) substance occurring naturally in the Earth's crust. Minerals are made up of either one element or mixtures of elements, called compounds. The hardness of a mineral is graded on a scale of 1 to 10. For instance talc is the softest and is graded with the number 1, whilst apatite is 5, quartz 7 and diamond is the hardest with a grade of 10. You might find it interesting that both talc and diamond are classified as crystals, illustrating the diversity of this form. Most minerals form crystals.

'Gemstone is the collective name for all ornamental stones. They are minerals which are valued for their beauty, rarity and durability. There are about 100 types, the most valued including diamonds and rubies.

'Many people may be very surprised to learn how much crystals and crystalline structures affect our daily lives. For a start, most people are unaware that they are literally made of crystal. Apatite, the mineral part of bone, is composed of microscopic calcium phosphate crystals and it is this crystal deposit which makes bone hard. Tooth enamel is made of the same substance. Some researchers have even noted similarities between our internal functioning and the properties of liquid crystals.

'Crystals are everywhere. Sugar forms crystals which are soluble, while soda crystals, also soluble, are used for cleaning purposes. Snowflakes are crystals which form when air temperature is below freezing in a region where water vapour condenses. The vapour changes directly to ice without passing through the liquid state. Every single one of the ice crystals – snowflakes – formed in this process is different from all the others – something to think about perhaps when the next snow falls.

'Salt crystals are soluble and best known as a food flavouring. They are also used to preserve food, as in Parma ham, and play an important part in the functioning of our bodies and also in the functioning of an electrode. It's all to do with what is called "ionic bonding", the mechanism by which atoms stick together to form salt molecules and salt crystals. Ionic bonding occurs when electrons transfer from the outer electron shell of one atom to the outer electron shell of another that can accept electrons to fill it. The transfer leaves both atoms as charged particles called "ions".

'In the case of salt, when a sodium atom with a single electron in its outer shell combines with a chlorine atom which can accept another electron to make the maximum of eight in its outer shell, the result is that the sodium becomes a positively charged sodium ion and the chlorine becomes a negatively charged chloride ion. The force of attraction between the two opposite charges binds the ions together to form a salt molecule.

'A crystal of salt (sodium chloride) contains sodium and chloride ions arranged in a regular network that extends throughout the crystal. This network is called a "giant ionic lattice".

'A chemical reaction occurs when this crystal structure is dissolved in water, which causes the two types of ion to separate and thus conduct electricity. This same property of salt crystals to conduct electricity has important implications for the proper functioning of the body's cells as the body's cells are themselves bathed in saline.

'Certain crystals, especially quartz varieties, can convert mechanical pressure into electrical energy, an example being a record-player cartridge. They can also convert electrical energy into precise mechanical vibrations, as in earphones.

'The properties of crystals and gemstones do seem to transform ordinary energies into what appear to be more subtle energies, extraordinary energies if you like.

'A crystal at rest is in perfect balance. It is not shrinking, growing or otherwise changing, although, in common with all other matter, its atoms are oscillating or vibrating. But this balance is very susceptible to the slightest internal or external influence.

'I noted the "normalizing" potential value of a material which has very predictable reactions to an external stimulus such as an electromagnetic pulse.'

Harry had vaguely heard that crystals had been used in natural healing for thousands of years and wondered whether this particular property of crystal could be anything to do with it. He says:

'I knew that most scientists would be sceptical of any suggestions that crystals can be used for healing purposes, especially in the absence of any attempt at an explanation within the parameters of conventional science.

'So I set about experimenting with crystals in order to see what they could do therapeutically and, at least as importantly, to find an acceptable explanation in order to satisfy any criticisms from scientific colleagues.'

(For a maverick inventor, Harry has many moments of quite unrestrained scientific conservatism.)

He experimented with putting a small electrical field through the crystals and examining their energy field with his Kirlian camera:

'The crystals gave off enormous amounts of energy when I stimulated and measured them with Kirlian photography and other instruments. In fact, it was during this period that I think I first measured the crystal entity energies. In some crystals there would be very unexpected things going on energetically and I started to ponder whether they might have "a life of their own".'

Harry also pondered what the therapeutic effects of this change in the crystals' energy field might be:

'I then used the Kirlian apparatus to see the effects of the energized crystals on the human body. I studied these effects for years, comparing the effects with those of natural crystals. The energized crystals had very different effects from the natural crystals.

'Then I found that by stimulating different crystals with certain compatible frequencies you could amplify each crystal's effects. In other words, each crystal harmonically resonated with particular frequencies.

'Applying the energized crystals to the body, I found that the energy distortions I saw in ESM radio-sound scans or Kirlian images would diminish and sometimes go altogether, with a consequent diminution of symptoms.'

Harry wondered why this should be and began yet more experiments. Now, many years later, he is an acknowledged scientific expert on the therapeutic properties of crystals. He tells us that:

'Crystals cause changes in brainwave patterns which can be measured on EEG monitors. If you hold a crystal in your hand the frequency of your own macro-molecules, which resonate a complex wave-form, can imprint itself into the otherwise regular oscillations of the crystal lattice. So the crystal's electrons will move in regular fashion, vibrating exactly like your own macro-molecules. The crystal appears to copy your own specific wave-form.

'If you heat a crystal you get electrical energy. If you squeeze it you get light. If you introduce a certain impurity you get a particular visible wavelength (colour).

'Subtle changes in the coating of a crystal can be used to detect very small changes in frequency caused by linking an antibody to a specific pesticide like malathion.

'Crystals can be placed over meters in houses to regulate pollution from "negative" energies. Crystals are even used to measure changes in radio wavelengths and can receive and amplify complicated wave-forms from miles away.

'Many crystal structures will respond in very precise ways to a wide range of energies including electricity, heat, light, pressure, sound, gamma rays, microwaves, bioelectricity and even what we might call "consciousness" energies such as thought.

'In response to these various introduced energies, the lattice structure of the crystal vibrates in different ways and gives out other energies. Given these phenomena, it should come as no surprise that crystals are very sensitive indeed to the subtlest of energy changes.

'Crystals can also amplify specific harmonics, and in this lies the basis of electro-crystal therapy. Given the premise that disease is characterized by a cell or a group of cells going "out of tune", then the action of a crystal is to receive the correct healthy signal and rebroadcast it, so that the specific "normal" wavelength can be pushed back into the cell and thus carry out a retuning function.

'And the effect does not appear to be limited to existing

cells. It seems that new cells born in the presence of the "correct" vibration know how to be healthy.'

Excited by his early results, Harry experimented with many different types of crystals. He would eventually decide to put a selection of small crystal chips of seven different colours in the test tube with the saline solution *(see Appendix)*. As with his ESM diagnosis and therapy work, the current from the Tesla coil in the electro-generator would travel from the generating unit, through an insulated wire, to the saline-filled tube, the electrode. Here it would cause the salt water electrolyte to give the crystals an 'ionic jacuzzi', as Harry calls it. This bubbling bath would, in effect, cause the crystals to 'vibrate'. Harry says:

'Vibration is a good word to describe what is actually happening. The pulses from what I then called the "electro-crystal" generator cause the crystals to expand and contract very rapidly as their outer ions gain and lose electrons over and over again in the ionic jacuzzi.

'This vibration induces the "secondary field effect", which basically means that it vibrates the energy field and the cells of the subject, giving the patient a tune-up in the right place with the right combination of crystals and energy. In this way we were able to mimic the healing effect of energy therapies on the body, but with two important differences.

'The first was that the machine did not rely on the practitioner. It worked whoever was using it.

'Secondly, the machine was able to induce a very specific and precise vibration into the patient's energy field. We found we could now target different areas of the body and the energy imbalances associated with different diseases by combining very specific normalizing frequencies with the crystal oscillators. The implications of this were obvious: over time it would be possible to find the right treatment combinations by trial and error.

'All this is very subtle, of course. You do not see the salt water bubbling, you do not see the crystals jiggling about and you will probably not hear any sound. But this certainly does not mean that nothing is happening. The electrode is placed on the body and the electrical energy from the generator is induced into the body – but there's no actual electrical contact with the body.

'The electrode is an insulator called a dielectric. Today we use a flexible silicone tube but, in those days, the crystals and saline were sealed in a test tube then energized with pulsed high frequency. This "excited" the crystals. They would then vibrate and get energized. When they're energizing they produce the secondary effect by induction into adjacent tissue which is also full of salty (conductive) fluids. It is these electrolytes in the body at a cellular level that get excited by the electro-crystal therapy. Later I called this a "molecular massage".'

The electro-crystal marriage appeared to promote balance, health and well-being in humans, animals and plants. Putting energy into the energy fields of living organisms via the crystal electrode seemed to cause a measurable change in the physical body which could not be achieved in the absence of the crystals.

Large numbers of therapists and patients have reported regular and repeatable beneficial results with this gentlest of therapies.

During the course of his research, Harry found that crystals have many other scientific applications which are sometimes not initially appreciated. In fact, as R. and V. Baer tell us in their book, *Windows of Light: Quartz Crystals and Self-Transformation* (Harper and Row, 1984),

'Quartz crystals can be used in many different ways to process various types of energy. These functions are numerous and include reception, reflection, refraction, magnification,

transduction, amplification, focusing, transmutation, trans-
ference, transformation, storage, capacitance, stabilization,
modulation, balancing and transmittance.'

Harry expands on this:

'Piezoelectricity is commercially significant and has been
extensively used since it was first discovered. During World
War I the piezoelectric effect was used to produce underwater
acoustic waves as an early form of submarine-detector sonar.

'Early on in the development of wireless technology, it
was found that when two quartz crystal slices of the same
size were subjected to 12 volts, both would react by vibrating at 2,169 vibrations per second. It did not take the
scientists long to realize that this had implications for
communication. The original crystal radio sets could only
"talk" to other sets with same size quartz crystal slice in them.

'Later, synthetic quartz was used in timepieces. The
slices of micro-thin synthetic quartz in watches and clocks
vibrate at 32,768 times per second. The crystal requires very
little power supply from a tiny battery, or an accumulator in
the case of solar-powered devices. As the atoms in the
quartz vibrate they emit very precise electronic pulses.
These pulses are channelled through microchip circuitry,
where their frequency is successively halved in a series of
15 steps. The result is a single constant pulse each second.

'The opposite or "inverse" piezoelectric effect is produced when a quartz plate is subjected to an alternating
electrical charge. The crystal will alternately expand and
contract, or vibrate, at a precise frequency. Arranged for this
purpose, a crystal oscillator circuit controls the frequency
bands in radio transmitters.'

The inverse piezoelectric effect is the property that Harry
employed in his electro-crystal therapy. The pulsed high-frequency electromagnetically-induced charge from his electro-crystal

generator excites or vibrates each one of the 100 or so crystal chips in the electrode by making it expand and contract between one and many thousand times a second, depending on the settings on the dials.

The various properties of crystals could easily explain why they work so well in the channelling of healing energies. Detractors, and we have come across many, who blithely state that they 'don't believe in crystal balls and all that nonsense' may not have had access to the work of people such as Marcel Vogel, a senior scientist with IBM for three decades, who studied the properties of crystals in great detail. Harry explains Dr Vogel's work:

'The key concept which Dr Vogel presented is that a quartz crystal is capable of amplifying and directing the natural energies of the healer. He believes that the subtle energies of the healer's field become focused and coherent in a manner similar to a laser.

'Ordinarily, light is incoherent, with rays of energy moving randomly in many directions at once. In the ruby laser, the crystal creates an amplification effect by organizing rays of light into a coherent, orderly beam that has a tremendously powerful energetic effect. Dr Vogel suggests that a natural quartz crystal works similarly to focus the subtle energies of the healer.'

Harry later encountered another variation on crystals and their interaction with the world of light around them. He learned that the subtle energy workings of a crystal can be observed by use of a hologram technique.

A hologram is a 3-D light image made with a laser. Early experiments showed that when a hologram of a crystal is made it still has an energy link with the solid material crystal. The method Harry used was to wire a crystal to a high impedance device and then 'influence' the hologram image. The results showed that large impedance changes occurred during the experiments.

Harry explains the significance:

'The "influences" employed were sunlight, human hands on the hologram and even thought direction. Not only does this border on mind/matter experiments, but it also shows a definite physical bond between a 3-D light image created via the hologram method and the physical object itself, which can be disturbed by brain-induced vibrations.

'These results were not inconsistent with my hypothesis that effects induced by brainwaves can be created in hologrammatic form. Most physicists would probably take a sceptical view of any claims that inorganic quartz crystals and organic matter, i.e. people, could have some form of communicative connection, even though the valency [electrical properties] of the silicon in the crystal and that of the carbon in the organism are both four.'

Whether there can be communication between the crystal and human kingdoms or not, there has certainly been a close historical relationship. Harry told us something of it:

'We humans have found many uses for crystals throughout the ages. Crystals stand the test of time. They tell us about the practices of the people who used and wore them. They were used as weapons, tools, ornaments, talismans, make-up, elixirs and in all manner of other ways.

'From prehistoric times we know that gems and precious stones have been revered. We have found them in ancient monuments and other sites where people congregated. The earliest uses were as tools and weapons. Some current estimates put the first use of stone tools at 1.8 million BC. By contrast the earliest metal object is currently dated at 4000 BC.

'At some point early people discovered a property of quartz called "conchoidal fracture" – when two pieces of flint [a form of quartz] are struck together they may fracture and produce a curved, shell-like edge as sharp and effective as steel. This discovery allowed our ancestral scientists to fashion tools and weapons instead of simply finding suitable material by chance.

'Flint also exhibits piezoelectricity, so that when mechanical pressure, say, from striking, is applied to it, a static electric charge is produced that generates a spark. Perhaps as long ago as one million BC, this technique was used to make the first intentional fire. A million or more years later we ignite dried pieces of plants rolled up in paper by employing the same principle in a cigarette lighter. Some pilot lights in gas cookers and fires work in a similar way.

'For centuries the wealthy have adorned themselves with stones of different hues which they openly displayed as status symbols. Crystals were forms of wealth and status before buildings, banking and credit cards.

'Of course diamonds and gems are still important "portable" wealth, but are not as essential as they once were as a means of exchange. But this does not mean that crystalline forms have lost their importance in commerce – far from it. Today, smart cards and all sorts of other financial instruments rely on crystal technology.

'So do our roads and buildings – they are constructed from crystalline material such as granite and marble. Concrete's rigidity and quick-setting properties depend on crystal growth.'

We wondered about the more mystical tradition surrounding crystals. Harry said:

'For hundreds of years crystals and gemstones were used to promote recovery from illness by placing them somewhere in the sickroom, on the ill person's body or by crushing them to a powder and then swallowing. But, gradually, more and more curative and mystical powers were attributed to them. They symbolized heavenly bliss, protected against poverty, killed venomous creatures, demonstrated faithfulness and could even keep the wearer out of prison.

'It is, perhaps, little wonder that their early therapeutic successes became confused with more mystical and esoteric concepts so that at the dawn of the "age of reason and science", about 300 years ago, they were all but discredited amongst conventional scientists.

'But the earlier mystical application of crystals can be seen in megalithic sites all around the world. These sacred sites are thought to be aligned by straight lines known as leys. Some people believe these leys are Earth meridians, carrying an energy like the *ch'i* of Chinese acupuncture between the stone sites. The sites themselves are thought to be Earth vortices where the energy configures like the chakras of the Indian Vedic tradition. Solar and lunar phenomena are also linked to these sites.

'Alfred Watkins of Hereford was the first modern observer to notice that ancient sites can be connected by straight lines. His notion was that they were ancient traders' routes, showing business people the way between potential groups of customers – but then he was a practical businessman!

'All we can provisionally conclude about stone sites and the straight lines linking them is that they do indeed appear to have had both scientific and mystical purposes, some of which depend on their being constructed of crystal.

'For example, the Men en tol (Hole in Stone) site at Land's End has two great legends associated with it. One is that the stone was an oracle which could be consulted. Two crossed needles would be placed on top of the stone by the wise person of the village. The questioner would ask the question. The needles would move and give an answer, interpreted by the seer.

'The other legend was that it was a healing stone. This is a tradition associated with a number of megalithic sites. At Men en tol a sick person would be passed through the large hole in the stone three times and then dragged around it nine times. This was a practice intended to promote healing, a property that local people had associated with the stone since before anyone can remember.

'A particular disease this technique was thought to cure was rickets, a bone disorder particularly common in the Middle Ages, when this site was still being used for healing. We know today that electromagnetism helps bone healing, so there might be a possibility that this and similar stone sites have geomagnetic properties.'

Harry once featured on a TV programme called *Earth Mysteries*, screened during 1983 and presented by Paul Devereux. As part of the programme, Harry and his colleagues measured changes in magnetic fields around different stones at different times. This leads some Earth mysteries researchers to conclude that there could be some degree of truth in the ancient legends about the mystical, healing and astronomical functions of the sites. Harry says:

'Whatever the substance or otherwise in the legends, it is undeniable that our ancestors utilized certain unique properties of crystals and stones in relation to magnetism. One example is the invention of the compass. Magnetite – or lodestone – is very magnetic. Twelfth-century mariners found that a piece floated on a stick in water aligned itself to the North Star.

'If we eliminate the idea of Atlantis for the purposes of this discussion, the early Egyptians appear to have been the first civilization to develop the use of crystals for cosmetics, such as eye make-up. They used to pound and powder green malachite and blue lapis lazuli. They then mixed the dust with olive oil and adorned their eyes with the paste. They applied the turquoise substance with a great deal of ritualistic reverence. One idea is that this "cosmetic" was an attempt to make themselves more "cosmic" by aligning themselves with nature, the cosmos. I have another – they may have learned by experiment or accident that green and blue crystals were good for balancing and healing the eyes.

Over time they would have noticed that they made people more attractive and there we may have the early origin of make-up.

'Also, one of the earliest known references to the healing power of crystals was some notes made on papyrus by an Egyptian scribe in 1600 BC.'

This document, only recently found by archaeologists, gives directions as to how to use crystals to cure ailments. The idea seems to have been to wear beads of lapis lazuli, malachite and red jasper around the neck when sick, so that the disease could pass through the crystals and dissipate – the negative energy would be 'channelled' out of the person by the crystal. This is a remarkably similar notion to Harry's modern one of crystals 'as energy transducers which have an ability to change energy from one form to another'.

Harry continues:

'In ancient Israel, Aaron, the brother of Moses, wore 12 gems on a ceremonial religious breastplate to represent the 12 tribes of Israel, signify his power and to bring good fortune.

'However, because ancient people did not always classify gemstones by mineral species like we do in modern times, there is some debate about which gemstones were set in the breastplate and why.'

Many gem scholars agree that the tradition of birthstones arose from this Breastplate of Aaron.

Harry continued with his explanation:

'As for crystal weaponry, black obsidian was used in arrow heads by the Vikings because of its energy-depleting proper-ties. Interestingly, the North Americans used the same sub-stance in the same way. Speculation that the Vikings and North Americans were trading with each other long before

Columbus is growing in academic circles. Perhaps they did indeed exchange ideas as well as goods.

'The use of crystal weaponry has become more sophisticated in the twentieth-century. We have already mentioned the use of crystals in World War I. In World War II, when bombs hit the ground, piezoelectric crystals within their noses converted the mechanical pressure to the electrical charge needed to detonate the device.

'As we approach the twenty-first century, the silicon chip communications revolution has huge implications for mega-sophisticated warfare and espionage. Same theme unfortunately – we like fighting – just a different way of using crystals to help us hurt each other.

'Some Christians say that crystals are mystical and dangerous and should be avoided. Perhaps we should ask whether it is the crystals themselves or the use we humans put them to that is the real problem.'

Harry demonstrates the natural effects of a crystal on the human energy field on all of his courses at the School of Electro-Crystal Therapy. He asks a student to stand and face Jane while he stands behind the student. 'Please close your eyes,' he instructs. He then places the point of a large quartz crystal, about the size of a big carrot, on the student's back, behind the heart chakra.

Harry begins to rotate the crystal clockwise, with the point gently making an ever-increasing circle on the student's shirt. The student will begin to sway slightly.

Once Harry has connected with the energy field, he pulls and pushes the crystal in and out. The student rocks back and forth in line with Harry's movements. Everyone is amazed at the effect that the 'dead' piece of rock can have on someone's energy field.

Harry says that in his experiments on volunteers, an anti-clockwise circular motion has caused buckling at the knees, as a form of earthing seems to take place. Trying this experiment for ourselves, we found that people also reported seeing lights and feeling tired, while others swayed and rocked as in Harry's demonstration.

Harry also often demonstrates the *natural* draining effect of a substance such as black obsidian. He asks a student volunteer to stand up and stretch out their dominant arm. He then applies downward pressure on the arm with his forefinger, telling them to resist. Most people can put up considerable resistance and Harry is usually unable to push the arm down.

He then asks the volunteer to hold a piece of black obsidian in the dominant hand for a minute or so and repeats the test. Much to their own surprise, and that of the group, very few people are then able to resist the downward pressure from his finger.

Although this weakening effect of the obsidian is very transitory, Harry generally offers a stimulating crystal to counteract it. Within moments the strength of the person returns and Harry repeats the finger-pressure experiment a third time to illustrate the recovery.

Harry stresses that a great deal of responsibility is required when conducting experiments of this nature. 'Very strong natural forces are at work. In the hands of an inexperienced or unscrupulous practitioner this is dangerous knowledge.'

Certainly in the past gems were considered to have mysterious powers. As well as being worn as talismans, gemstones were also thought to give protection from ghosts and prejudice angels and saints in the wearer's favour.

The Christian Church has always had a rather ambivalent stance towards crystals and the superstitions surrounding them. Yet in *The Book of Crystal Healing* (Gaia Books, 1997), Liz Simpson tells us that 'In the Bible stones and rocks were a symbol of the human spirit and a representation of the higher Self. Christ is referred to as a "living stone".'

She also informs us that the custom of wearing amulets as protection against evil spirits and illness was not without its sceptics. When the jester at the court of the Holy Roman Emperor Charles V (1500–58) was asked what was the amuletic property of turquoise, he replied that if you happened to fall from a high tower while wearing it, the turquoise would remain unbroken!

The same scepticism is not apparent in the life of Pope Clement VII who, in the late sixteenth century, is reputed to have ingested a gem concoction worth 40,000 ducats – equivalent to more than two million pounds today.

During the Renaissance, efforts were made to find a reason for the belief that these stones had special powers. Paracelsus, a well-known mystic and physician of the sixteenth century, claimed that his talismanic jewel had a spirit attached whom he called Azoth, while Native Americans too believed quartz crystals to be the home of supernatural forces. They hoped these spirits would bring good luck to their hunting expeditions and 'fed' them periodically by wiping the crystals with fresh deer's blood.

Comparisons between these historical beliefs and the PIP scanner's discovery of crystal-dwelling photonic beings are unavoidable. As we know, Harry Oldfield has actually *filmed* these beings moving around on top of crystals and darting in and out of them. He has found that they exist in about 10 per cent of crystals.

'They particularly like a quartz environment,' he tells us matter of factly. Not surprisingly, Harry considers the discovery of this silicon-based life-form as the greatest discovery made with his PIP scanner to date.

Turning to the future, Harry often speculates on the ways in which we may soon make use of crystals:

'The nanotechnology of the future might create material atom by atom. This idea was first conceived by Richard Feynman in 1959. In nature, pure elemental carbon can be either rock-hard diamond or soft graphite, depending on the precise structure/pattern of its atoms.

'Work is in progress to produce the even more sophisticated computer-aided design tools necessary for the manipulation and production of crystalline material, particularly diamond, atom by atom, molecule by molecule.

'Diamond is both the hardest natural substance on the planet and very light in comparison to metals such as steel, so one intention is to build, from diamond-like material, aircraft that are one-hundredth the weight but 10,000 times the strength they are at present.

'In Japan, a nanotechnology revolution is in progress. The race is on to make diamond from natural gas at low pressure.

'It has been speculated that the early part of the twenty-first century will be known as the Diamond Age.'

As for the present uses of crystals, Harry told us something of how they are used in determining the origin of substances and artefacts:

'Dr Olwen Williams-Thorpe of the Open University wanted to investigate the origin of the granite Roman columns which were transported to Windsor Park in the nineteenth century. Granite is a naturally radioactive crystal substance composed of uranium, potassium and thorium.

'The different composition of each piece of granite provides a chemical fingerprint in the form of gamma ray emissions. This means that the precise origin of a piece of granite can be deduced by matching its radiation fingerprint with the known fingerprints of all the quarries around the world.

'Dr Williams-Thorpe believed that the Windsor Park columns may have originally come from Leptus Magna, a Roman town and quarry in North Africa. She used a gamma ray spectrometer, known as a GR256, to detect the chemical fingerprints from granite emissions. A probe is part of the equipment.'

Dr Williams-Thorpe herself explains:

'The end of the probe is crystal, mostly sodium. The gamma rays zap into the crystal. When they enter it they produce tiny flashes of light. Essentially the interaction of the gamma rays with the crystal structure enables us to measure the intensity of each flash of light and to count the number of flashes.

'The computer in the spectrometer matches the Windsor Park granite with that of all known sites. The data confirmed that the columns originally came from Leptus Magna and were used in buildings in north-west Turkey in the period from the first to the fourth century.'

Dr Williams-Thorpe's spectrometer utilizes the special relationship between crystals and light. Harry told us more about this relationship:

'Just a few atoms per million can change the perfect internal structure of a crystal enough to colour it. As an illustration, we can imagine a cube of quartz crystal (composed of silicon and oxygen atoms) one foot square. By introducing a collection of a few iron atoms, the relative size of a pin head, Mother Nature can turn the quartz violet and so it becomes amethyst.

'Whilst the iron atom is nearly the same size as a silicon atom, putting it in the space that was meant for the silicon atom is like trying to put a size 6 foot in a size $5^1/2$ shoe. Whilst it still fits, it pinches. This "pinch" has the effect of "trapping" all light vibrations except that of violet. Hence the violet ray is transmitted to give the characteristic colour of amethyst. Science is still undecided as to how the atoms actually "trap" the light, though recently they have discovered more about the process.'

Harry is very interested in this subject. He began by telling us that physicists have proved for the first time a theory which predicted that high density light can become trapped inside objects which would normally diffuse rays to give them their white colour:

'The diffuse scattering of light is a common phenomenon, occurring among other things in white paint, fog and clouds. For example, in snowflakes, the rays of light are reflected from one crystal of ice to another, creating the white colour, before finding their way out again.

'Theorists had predicted that when scattering became intense, with only tiny distances between the reflections, the light waves would interfere with each other and become trapped in the material. They called this process "Anderson localization".

'At the European Laboratory for Non-Linear Spectroscopy in Florence, scientists have actually created and witnessed Anderson localization for light, using gallium arsenide powder – which is the substance we chose for our opto-crystal therapy machines years ago *[see Chapter 6]*.

'The scientists said that this substance "traps what we might call the semi-frozen light, which keeps on running around in random loops and so never leaves the material". This is the first time that science has been able to achieve this effect.'

We asked Harry to comment further on the importance of light:

'The Anderson effect can literally allow us to see crystals in a different light. The concept of photophoresis is important to this discussion. This is the idea that light travels in spirals. It has long been of interest to me. You see, if light travels in spirals then it is travelling at a different speed at the eye of the spiral than it is at the wider end. This would have profound implications for the belief that there is only one speed of light.

'It may be that the photonic presence in an atom gives the illusion of a particle when really it's a field. The subject is complicated and there is a lot of disagreement, but some of my work with crystals is very much related to the properties of light, so I'm very interested in all these developments.'

Harry's open-minded approach and curiosity about the invisible universe of energy and vibration brings him into contact with a growing number of people with the same enquiring spirit. Indeed, many people seem to be desperate for a kindred spirit, with knowledge and understanding, to point them in the right direction and reassure them that the future holds a rational explanation for their 'insanity'.

This is illustrated on another day of research at Harry Oldfield's clinic. Grant is sitting at the portable computer which rests precariously on a wobbly little table in a noisy hallway. It's not an ideal place to try to write a book but, as the only available space, it'll have to do. Harry is on the phone and Grant cannot help overhearing his conversation.

'Yes, there have been lots of reported experiences of crystals disappearing from this physical dimension and reappearing in the same place some time later. In California's Death Valley the stones reportedly move around in the desert by themselves, leaving tracks in the sand as they do so.'

Harry listens intently as the caller speaks. 'No, I would certainly not accept people telling you that such things are not possible.'

The caller speaks again.

Harry reassures him further: 'Oh no, you're definitely not mad to consider the possibility!'

Something that worries many people is that some researchers have ascribed many unusual, even sinister, properties to crystals. Harry's view is that:

'This could be a case of researchers putting their own superstitions and fears on to the poor old crystals. These sorts of ill-considered comments have left us the legacy of having to defend the use of crystals to this very day.

'But there is absolutely no evidence to support these accusations. In fact, the evidence suggests that the effect of crystals on human beings is generally positive, especially in the therapeutic sense.'

In this regard we asked Harry about that peculiar phenomenon, the crystal skulls, some of which are said to have been cursed. He replied:

'Yes, I have looked into that subject. The most interesting crystal skulls were discovered in South America.

'As to the date they were made, that's difficult. Quartz crystal is hard to date using conventional means because it's made of silicon, whereas carbon dating relies on something being made of carbon, as the term implies.

'As to usage, they were presumably very important because quartz crystal is very hard to sculpt. Given the amount of smoothness achieved and the detail involved, each could have taken generations to make.

'I think a crystal skull might have been used as a consciousness alteration device, perhaps for some sort of initiation rite or other very specific religious or spiritual purpose. I think the brain is very important. Perhaps the brain is a quantum mechanical device which not only radiates information within our mind/body system but could also be a transceiver for communication with "places" – if that's the right word – outside our own space-time continuum.

'We must remember that crystals are energy transducers that can turn one form of energy into another. They are also thought to be able to store information, a bit like memory, and appear to be able to induce altered states of consciousness. Perhaps these ancient native South Americans knew something of these properties.'

Others have noted the same effects. In *The Curious Lore of Precious Stones* (Lippincott, 1913), George Frederick Kunz tells us that those who gaze for a long time and without interruption on a crystal or glass ball, an opal, a moonstone, a sapphire or a cat's eye may become partially hypnotized or even fall into a profound sleep.

Kunz said that the condition induced, whether a semi-trance, a hypnotic trance, or simply due to the imaginative workings of the brain, is believed to give an insight into the future:

'This hypnotic effect is probably caused by some gleam or point of light in the stone attracting and fixing the behold-er's gaze. The moonstone, the star sapphire and the cat's eye are all gems which possess a moving light, a moving line, or three crossed lines, and they are believed by the Orientals to be gems of good luck.

'Indeed, it is supposed in the East that a living spirit dwells within these stones, a spirit potent for good.'

Kunz speculated that this was just 'imagination on the part of the Orientals' and that 'The "spirit" bears much the same relation-ship to the crystal as the shadow bears to a form.' However, this apparent put-down of the Oriental tradition may have been a lit-tle off the mark. For a start, animism, the belief that spirits or energies inhabit and animate 'inanimate' objects such as trees or rocks, is not just an Eastern concept, but may be one of humani-ty's most ancient beliefs. On his courses Harry always gives an overview of these concepts to put his work with the crystal enti-ties in context.

Some of the characteristics attributed to crystals and gems are obviously a little on the mystical side, but, as we discovered, some of the historical uses of crystals do seem to be firmly based on their accepted scientific properties.

The scientific utilization of crystals caught Harry's attention very early on. He was 18 when the silicon chip was invented in 1971. Harry remembers:

'The silicon wafer had come into common usage at that time and was now known as "the silicon chip". A silicon chip is a piece of almost pure silicon, usually less than one centimetre square and about half a millimetre thick. It contains hundreds of thousands of micro-miniature electronic circuits, mainly transistors, packed and interconnected in layers beneath the surface. On the surface there is a grid of twin metallic strips which are connections – via wires – to the outside world.

'There are three main types of silicon chips: microprocessor chips perform arithmetical and logical functions, memory chips store information, and communications chips enable a computer to interact with the user, for example, the keyboard and TV screen.

'There were silicon chips everywhere in no time at all. It was a case of "chips with everything". They were in wrist watches, pocket calculators, television games, toys, home computers. The progress of silicon technology was incredible.

'The number of transistors which fitted onto a silicon chip about half a centimetre square in 1960 was just one. By 1970 it was one thousand and in 1979 it was one million. I remember one prediction at the time which suggested that by 1990 technology would be available with one billion transistors on each silicon chip.

'We all thought the implications were marvellous. I immediately started to find out as much as I could about the emerging technology and was able to incorporate it very soon into the electro-crystal therapy machines and so improve their performance and output.

'For example, the new types of circuit were much less prone to overheating and were much more compact. This meant we could produce very portable versions. Later, improvements in computer technology facilitated the development of the PIP system.

'This silicon technology made it easy for me to accept that crystals may be able to channel healing energies into a patient, since they were so good at doing a similar thing inside computers.'

So, after many experiments, Harry knew that crystals could help people naturally and he also knew that they had many useful properties that were both technological and scientifically verifiable. The task he had initially set himself was to come up with a combination of the natural and the scientific which would help people to balance their subtle energy fields. By the early 1980s, crystals had become a fundamental part of this pioneering work.

Shortly afterwards Harry was fast gaining a reputation as a therapist who was obtaining some very interesting results.

Prediction magazine, in its November 1984 issue, gave a good indication of Harry's progress when, in reply to the reader's question 'Who is the healer Harry Oldfield and how does he practise his art, please?' it described Harry as 'a remarkable young man with what many believe is an even more remarkable future'. Prophesy indeed!

THERAPY

'First, do no harm.'

HIPPOCRATES

I N October 1982, Harry and Eileen moved to South Ruislip.
It was a busy time for them. Eileen had been working to support Harry's research. The electro aspects of the research
had involved refining the frequencies emanating from the generator and the crystal research had highlighted which crystals had
the optimum effect. The resulting *electro-crystal* therapy was very
different from *crystal* therapy in that Harry's idea was to mix
pulsing frequencies – which had been used in hospitals to such
good effect with bone healing and ultrasound techniques – with
the natural therapeutic effects of the crystals.

Harry is fond of saying that the 'masculine' electro 'Father
Sky' energy and 'feminine' crystal 'Mother Earth' aspects of his
work came together in 'marriage'. The 'offspring', born in 1982,
was a child christened 'electro-crystal therapy' by its guardian
in 1983.

Harry found he could actually enhance the natural healing
effect of the crystals many times over by pulsing electromagnetic
energy through the seven different coloured crystals he experimented with. He had also found that when he pulsed electromagnetic energy on its own, just using a saline solution in a tube to
conduct the energy into the human system, it only worked in a
very limited way on pain and inflammation. When, however, he
put a 'rainbow'-coloured collection of about 100 tiny crystals in

the saline solution in the tube, the therapeutic effect was extended to include many more conditions.

Finally, when Harry had worked out the correct frequency settings on his dials for each of the seven energy zones (the chakra energy centres), he found he could treat a huge range of conditions very specifically by targeting them with the correct restorative frequency. He had found a way to open his healing 'windows'.

So it was that a composite technique using an energy source of pulsed high-frequency electromagnetism and a 'natural' electrode made with crystal chip oscillators in conductive saline solution emerged into the world. Once it had been comprehensively tested on different parts of the body and for different disease states, Harry was satisfied that he could start offering treatment to the general public.

The Oldfields spent a few months planning the next move forward for the work. The Clinic and School of Electro-Crystal Therapy were formed to teach, develop and generally promote electro-crystal therapy and were launched in 1983. But this was not the only new project. Less than a year later, Eileen fell pregnant. She and Harry were soon to be blessed with a son, Anthony.

Harry was meantime very quickly recognized both at home and abroad as a practitioner who was achieving some amazing results. Prestigious publications reported his positive results in treating people with a wide spectrum of complaints and it was speculated that a large number of injuries and illnesses could be treated with the 'crystal energies'.

But Harry Oldfield was not concerned with fame and fortune, worldly recognition and so on. Long ago, he identified himself with the healing mission of Jesus Christ. Harry says:

'Jesus Christ is a very special friend. He's a constant inspiration in my work. I made a dedication to Him long ago. Then, when I got frustrated with being able to show people how ill they were without being able to help them, I said to the Lord how I would have loved to have gone out and healed the sick just as He did.

'When I read the passage in the Bible where Jesus commanded His disciples to go out and heal the sick and preach the Kingdom of God, I knew that He was speaking to me personally. I also decided to do it in the same order as He did – heal first, preach second. And I decided that, if I could get the tools together, then this would be a way to help people heal. I think He might have heard my prayer as He seems to have been giving me the tools ever since. My inspiration is often the direct result of prayer.'

As part of this approach, Harry has always done his best to avoid treatment fees for children, people with life-threatening diseases and the guardians of distressed animals. However, perhaps because of his kindly and caring approach, many of these people or their representatives often choose to give a donation to his research. He continues:

'A healing idea can be in a million or more places at once, and I wanted to find ways of spreading healing as far and wide as possible. As I don't consider myself to have any natural healing ability, and it is difficult to be in more than one place at once, I set myself a task: to invent, construct and produce a natural healing device that could be used, like a sort of electronic tuning fork, by beginners and virtuosos alike, to tune a delicate musical instrument, the complex system of matter, energy and conscious mind that we call a human being.

'I spent a great deal of time researching which frequencies would combine with the crystals to achieve the best tuning effects. My aim from the outset was to produce devices that would be effective and inexpensive as well as simple to use.'

Harry's 'magic machine', as it has since been dubbed, can certainly be tried and tested by anyone who cares to take the time and trouble to review its merits under properly controlled conditions.

In one of his favourite teaching analogies for students, Harry Oldfield describes the human being 'as a musical instrument designed and made by God':

'God invented the music of life and the instruments on which it is played. Each player is entrusted with an instrument on temporary loan and, in this role of custodian, manages, through a mixture of learning and experience, to play God's music with varying degrees of beauty and harmony.

'Think of a person as a violin. The wood and clasps of a violin are a certain physical shape and size, they are the physical body of the instrument. The four strings can be thought of, in our current analogy, as the etheric (or the physical body's energy double), mental, emotional and spiritual energy bodies.

'To get a sound, a conscious musician needs to actually pick up and play the instrument. So we can think of our bodies as instruments or "vehicles of expression" for that part of ourselves which is really calling the tune – the conscious musician or mind.'

Harry continues with his musical theme when talking about health and well-being:

'For various reasons, even the best kept instrument is always going to get a little squeaky and will need regular retuning. And if the conscious custodian of the instrument treats it very carelessly, or if luck, fate or chance take a hand, a physical part may become damaged or even break. Glue, tape, varnish and even replacement parts – orthodox medicine – may be deemed necessary to restore the instrument to its former glory. But if the damage is too severe, no amount of loving restoration will be enough and the instrument will just not play the same way as it did before. So perhaps prevention rather than cure should be our first aim.'

Indeed, Harry discovered that by treating the human being as an instrument in need of a regular 'energy retune', amazing results could be achieved in the prevention of disease, alleviation of symptoms in existing disease, and general maintenance of a healthy balance between the energetic and the physical systems. (Nowadays more and more people are using Harry's machines to stay well balanced and 'in tune' rather than waiting until they are ill.) The positive results held true for babies, animals, fish and even plants, so could not be explained away as a mere 'placebo effect'. In many cases, 'psychosomatic' or 'mind over matter' explanations could be discounted too, since it was obvious, certainly to Harry, that it was his energy treatments that were causing the positive effects.

To go back to the musical analogy, Harry says:

'The human instrument has a scale of seven notes on which we each play our own version of God's music. This scale is often called the chakra system. The seven main chakras are represented by seven colours.

'Often, in the descriptions I have seen, the seven colours are strictly represented as those of the rainbow, that is, red at the base of the spine then progressively up the body through orange, yellow, green, blue and indigo to violet at the crown of the head.'

However, from his measurements, Harry found what he believes to be changes in the human chakra system since they were first charted some 5,000 years ago in those ancient Sanskrit texts called the *Upanishads (see Appendix)*. He explains:

'One thought I have had on this is that Man's spiritual progress has evolved and this may have altered the nature of the spiritual bodies. Or the changes may be due to pollution, electromagnetic invasion and many other things.'

Harry adds an important proviso:

'I can only testify to my own research and results. In the case of concepts like chakras, for example, I have had to rely on descriptions previously set out by others. I have never seen the classic cone-shaped chakra on the PIP system, but that certainly does not mean that they do not exist as described. Neither is it to say that we will not see these phenomena when the imaging technology improves.

'What I can say is that the characteristics ascribed to the energy field in both ancient and modern descriptions have directed me down very fruitful avenues. Effective diagnostic and treatment techniques have been the result, so this certainly suggests there is something in these ideas.'

We were intrigued to know more about how Harry first came across the ancient ideas concerning chakras. After all, for a conventional Western scientist, these Eastern mystical concepts were, in a very real sense, a 'forgotten and foreign language'.

Apparently Harry had found the 'seven energy-configuration points' associated with the chakras without knowing what they were. Before this discovery, no one had ever claimed to have detected a chakra with a scientific instrument. Harry had found all seven, but been unaware of the significance of his discovery until a professor pointed it out to him.

Professor John Hasted was one of the leading academic critics in regard to the usefulness of Kirlian photography as a research tool. He was particularly critical of 'unscientific' protocols used, or not used, by many who called themselves researchers. Professor of Physics and Head of Faculty at Birkbeck College in London, in the early 1980s he had written a book about metal benders in an attempt to explain the phenomenon of people like Uri Geller. Harry remembers him as both 'open minded and a very stringent scientist'.

In 1982 Harry was invited to give a lecture at Birkbeck College before an audience of around 120 people. Just before he was about to start, the young man who had invited him came up to him and said, 'Er, Professor Hasted's here. You know what he has said and written about Kirlian, so you might want to take account of that.'

Harry was confident of his science and his findings, but nevertheless he did feel a little intimidated by the presence of such a vocal and respected critic of his subject. However, he lectured the massed group of scientists for about an hour, showing slides and experimental results and using his best scientific explanations for the phenomena observed.

Despite his best efforts, the lecture was received in total silence and at the end, no one clapped or made any gesture of appreciation.

Better grab my stuff and get out of here, Harry thought to himself. But then Professor Hasted rose to his feet.

Here it comes, worried Harry.

'Ladies and gentlemen,' began the professor, 'I would like to make a statement.' Suddenly he beamed at Harry and said, 'Up until this moment you all know that I have been a critic of the Kirlian technique because of its unscientific proponents. But this young man has obviously employed the most rigorous scientific methodology and I, for one, am prepared to state that I am much more enthusiastic about the potential of Kirlian research having seen today's presentation.'

With that, the professor began a slow clap. The whole faculty breathed a sigh of relief, as if on Harry's behalf, and began clapping enthusiastically.

This ordeal over, Harry was soon invited to give a talk to a much smaller gathering of senior scientists. This time he demonstrated his electro-scanning method which, as we know, uses the electromagnetic field around the body as a reference rather than trying to capture information on film as in the classic Kirlian method. Professor Hasted was again in the audience.

'Tell me, Mr Oldfield,' he queried, 'do you get a lot of fluctuations and anomalies when scanning?'

'Yes, I get readings showing an apparent configuration of the energies at seven points – one on top of the head, one on the brow, another in the throat area and so on down the front of the body in the area of the heart, solar plexus, navel and pelvic region. From my thousands of measurements, I can fairly confidently say that when we have an injury, a disease or some condition present we seem to get fluctuations in the associated energy-configuration point.'

'Very interesting. What about the back of the body?'

'Oh, yes, four of the configuration points also appear to have "mirror" configurations at the back. In other words, there appear to be four matching points on the spine behind the throat, heart, solar plexus and navel.'

'Very, very interesting,' mused the professor. 'Tell me, have you ever heard of the chakras?'

Harry's expression went blank. 'No,' he said, 'I can't say I have.'

'Well, Mr Oldfield, I do believe you have discovered, or rather rediscovered, the chakras. Perhaps we could talk about this further.'

After the lecture Harry had a private chat with Professor Hasted. He became both intrigued and excited as the Professor of Physics from the well-respected scientific institution began relating details of his own researches into the mysterious chakras, those mythical whirlwinds in the body's invisible energy atmosphere which the ancients had seen, called 'wheels' and depicted as flowers with petals.

John Hasted said:

'I first heard about the chakras through the case of a little boy who, whilst sitting at the family dinner table, said out loud, "Mummy, Mummy, the light in Uncle Willy's heart has gone out." That night, Uncle Willy died of a heart attack. The boy began regularly demonstrating similar feats of "insight" and his parents sought help. Eventually the boy was passed on to me and I performed tests on him.'

Harry added:

'Professor Hasted used a Faraday cage to eliminate outside electromagnetic energy influences from the results. In each experiment, the energy field of a volunteer was subjected to harmless bombardment with a stroboscopic light procedure. The boy was asked to say when the different energy centres stopped moving. In this way the harmonics of the chakras could be worked out for each particular volunteer.

'The same principle is employed to test the timing belt of a motorcar or to "freeze" the rotor blades of a helicopter. If you play a flickering light at the rotor blades and get the frequency right, it appears as if the rotor blades actually stop and so you can look at it to check for problems in its operation, structural deformations and so on. Stroboscopic procedures are standard techniques used in industrial engineering.'

Harry began his own experiments, consulted the *Upanishad* charts and satisfied himself that there are indeed seven energy-configuration centres or chakras for each person. He found that the seven points that he had described corresponded very closely to the traditional images depicting flowers at certain points around the body. Many modern investigators of this phenomenon postulate that the different numbers of petals on each of the flowers might relate to the different frequency or vibration associated with each of seven zones of the body.

In natural medicine around the world, these different vibrations have long been represented by the colours of the rainbow, starting with red, the lowest vibration, at the base and moving up through the visible light spectrum to violet at the crown. As mentioned earlier, since the chakras are connected with light in some way, it has been speculated that the people who drew those ancient charts were 'seeing' the chakras with their eyes. They may have been attuned to such vibrations. Harry has also wondered whether they may have been by-passing the normal eye/brain information processing system and directly sensing the chakra information with their 'mind/brain'. He said:

'Although we are all slightly different energetically in the same way that we are physically, these energy configuration centres are similar for everybody.

'When a person was unwell, we found that the associated chakra was out of balance relative to their own norm. It was then a matter of trial and error to find out the best vibrations to apply to each chakra to get a normalizing or balancing effect.

'Then we discovered that certain crystals had an empathy with certain chakras, depending on their colour or ray. And, rather amazingly to me at the time but not so much now, the colours corresponded to the colours depicted in those ancient books, although I must say we have found some modern variations on the original theme and I have a few theories about why this is so.

'In the main, I have been able to work out which vibrations and what crystals to use to balance each chakra to best effect. For example, red ruby and garnet are affiliated to the base chakra, the violet amethyst is affiliated to the brow chakra and orange carnelion and jasper are affiliated to the splenic (navel) chakra.

'And from a therapy point of view, as we said before, balancing the energy seems to help balance the physical cells. Or, to use our weather analogy, we employ our energy-generating machines to calm storms where there is too much turbulence in the body's invisible atmosphere and stir things up a bit when we come across an area which is in the doldrums. Even if everything is nice and balanced, mild and warm, we can still tweak the weather a little bit to ensure maintenance of the optimum climate for that particular person over the longer term.'

Harry has now tested many crystals to find out which work best with each chakra or zone of the body and, deciding that the number of petals in the chakra flower drawings may well represent harmonic frequencies, he based his frequency settings on them.

He later concluded that the 10,000 crown chakra petals – associated with our mind/brain/soul aspects – probably represented 'infinity' to the ancients, for whom 10 rows of 1,000 men were considered to be an 'infinite army'. Sometimes the crown chakra was represented as white rather than violet, indicating perhaps the crown's association with these higher universal aspects of ourselves. White embodies all the colours and vibrations and thus is thought to symbolize 'the whole'.

Harry came up with his own way of representing the chakras using colour coded zones on the body. In electro-crystal therapy the colours start with red at the base and go up through orange, green (not yellow), yellow (not green), blue, violet (not indigo) and white (not violet). This system is illustrated diagrammatically by Chakraman *(see plate section)*, who, despite the name, is meant to represent both male and female. It is this modernized chakra system on which both the 'electro compatibilities' and the 'crystal affinities' are based in electro-crystal therapy *(see Appendix)*.

To emit the 'correct' vibrations of each one of the seven chakra zones Harry could have used seven machines. He could also have used seven tubes each filled with the correct colour crystals. For example, the first machine would have been able to generate the lowest vibrations in the compatible frequency band for the base chakra and the energy would have been pulsed from the machine through red crystals which have an affinity with the base chakra zone. However, as Harry explains:

'It obviously made a great deal more sense to make one universal generating machine that could be tuned to any of the chakra frequency bands and, similarly, to have a universal crystal tube that would have an affinity with any of the chakra zones.'

The machine was christened the 'electro-crystal generator' and the multi-purpose tube was called the 'universal electrode', or 'crystal wand' if you prefer its nickname.

After much experimentation, Harry settled on a generating machine with three dials on the front and an off/on switch. One dial initiates the electromagnetic output. A second dial can be set to A, B, C or D, the frequency bands (an analogy would be the LW, MW, SW or FM bands, respectively, that you can tune your radio set to). The third dial, which can be set to any number between 0 and 10, is like the fine tuner on a radio set. It gives a great deal of precision as to which frequencies are pulsed into the crystals and thereby induced into the energy field of the person, animal or plant being treated.

Harry is always keen to point out the importance of the pulsed high-frequency electromagnetic energy waves which come from his machine. This pulsed energy is very different in its effect from ordinary high-frequency electromagnetic energy waves. Harry usually explains it thus:

'A pulsed high-frequency transmitter can be compared to a water tap with a bowl of water beneath it.

'If the tap is turned on fully, the water will start to swirl round the bowl and cause a waveless whirlpool-like effect.

'If, however, we almost turn the tap off, so that it drips separate water drops onto the surface of the water in the bowl, after the whirlpool has subsided the drips will send out waves continuously across the surface as they hit the water. These waves will be subject to all the rules of wave mechanics, such as harmonics, resonance, interference and so on. And, though we cannot vary the height of the tap from the bowl – without moving the bowl – we are able, by turning the tap gently, to control the repetition rate of the drips and hence the nature of the waves.

'By pulsing high-frequency waves we allow the waves' harmonics, that is, the multiples of a standard frequency, to have their maximum effect, because the gap between successive pulses allows each wave to express itself without interference from succeeding pulses. The highest harmonic possible will, theoretically, be infinite.

'Harmonics cannot develop from steady continuous high-frequency devoid of pulses, since there would be no gap in which they can do so.

'And by altering the space of the gap we can control the harmonics generated. If we multiply the frequency in Hertz – one Hz is equal to one cycle per second – by the number of pulses per second, we can see that large numbers of harmonics can be achieved, even on the simple assumption that only one harmonic is produced in each gap.'

Basically Harry is saying that the idea is to generate 'maximum harmonics with minimum energy input'. He often says that by a correct setting on his generating machine he is able to 'play a choir of harmonious voices in the correct range' into a person's energy field via the oscillating crystal amplifiers:

'The very clever human body energy system then "responds" to whichever of the multitude of notes it requires for healing.

'For example, we link the chakra system in electro-crystal therapy to the endocrine glands of the physical body and we have standard settings with which to tranquillize, balance or stimulate the energy and thus the glands.

'So, if we have a person with an underactive thyroid we use the stimulating frequency for the throat chakra, which is C5, in order to get the chakra energy vibrating faster and this has a corresponding effect on the physical thyroid gland.

'If someone has the 'flu we would stimulate the heart chakra to get the thymus gland working, since it is this gland that is involved with the immune system.

'Apart from "governing" or regulating the function of specific endocrine glands, each chakra is also associated with a particular part of the body. For example, the arms are "governed" by the throat chakra.

'I had a lady come to me with arthritic fingers. Her hands were like claws. I soon discovered that she had had a problem communicating something to someone and this repressed emotion, over time, had caused a blockage in the throat chakra energy which I was able to measure using ESM. The blockage in the flow of energy was then expressed, in a physical sense, by a stiffening and contraction of the fingers in her hands. This is a classic example of how the physical, mental, emotional and spiritual aspects of the self are linked.

'This is also shown by the effect that stress can have. Stress is a by-product of living in our modern world and a great deal of disease is attributable to it. But electro-crystal therapy can help break into the patterns of stress that have built up. Alpha rhythms have been found to be particularly useful in this respect, especially when applied to the area of the head in general and to the base of the brain in particular. With this technique we have had a lot of success in helping with stress, insomnia and panic attacks.

'In contrast, if someone is tired we may stimulate both the base and crown chakras with A5 and D5, respectively, to get their energy boosted up a bit.

'For more serious diseases we use combinations of settings. In a case of someone with cancer, for example, wherever the active site of cancer is, we attempt to keep it under control, stop it getting larger and hope to tip the balance in our favour all the time, to the point where the body finally vanquishes the growth itself.

'At the same time as calming the energy at the site of the tumour to stop the cells reproducing, we would boost the immune system, perhaps apply alpha rhythms to help with the inevitable stress, and generally try to balance the whole energy system so that the person is in the best state to cope with both the condition and some of the less gentle biochemical and surgical treatments that they are often undergoing.

'We have now developed a comprehensive table of settings intended as guidelines for treatment of the energetic imbalances associated with all kinds of diseases and conditions.

'We have also introduced a "family" of different electrodes containing various combinations of crystals for different conditions. The main development in this area was the introduction of a flexible silicone tube which could be safely and more easily applied to the body. For example, it could be bent and loosely knotted in many practical ways such as around the throat, knee, elbow or head.

'In any discussion of the therapy, I must make it clear that everyone is different and we treat each person holistically as an individual. For example, there is no such thing as ME but rather many different MEs – and the same is true for other states of dis-ease. Everyone has their own special set of energetic symptoms related to the physical, mental, emotional and spiritual aspects of their whole being.

'For instance, we will often find that someone with cancer has experienced a shock or trauma such as bereavement about 18 to 24 months before the disease took hold. I believe this is because the immune system is temporarily suppressed at the time of the trauma. This means that cancers can get a hold whereas normally the immune system would destroy the rogue cells very quickly. We aim to restart and support the immune system so that the body's natural defences can do their best.

'Individual human beings are far too complex for them all to be treated in the same way. Notwithstanding, there are, as I have said, certain tried and tested frequency settings we can combine with the crystals for certain diseases and conditions.

'The skill of the therapist is in knowing how and when to apply the different combinations.'

We have thus far discussed Harry's interpretation of the chakras and other characteristics of what is often called the etheric body, the energy body said to relate most to the physical. We should now give some consideration to his thinking with regard to the other subtle energy bodies postulated in many ancient and modern descriptions. Harry says:

'If the chakras represent a scale of seven notes, then the subtle bodies might be thought of as "octaves" which radiate out from the body. Some have said that these "subtle bodies" are not necessarily to be thought of as existing in our physical space-time environment. They could be "elsewhere", like dreams, operating in another place, another space-time or dimension or plane in which other things are going on about which we have no day-to-day understanding. Yet they still impact on us here and now by filtering down into the physical universe via the chakra system.

'This leads us back to the point of energy medicine in general and electro-crystal therapy in particular. We have learned that there may be seven notes, known as the seven chakras, and also several octaves of notes, known as the energy bodies.

'These "bodies" can be thought of as a succession of subtler and subtler atmospheres surrounding each of us. These atmospheres are often likened to those Russian dolls which fit inside each other, but we must always bear in mind that not all of them are necessarily in this space-time continuum.

'Each of these subtle atmospheres is thought to enable an aspect of our physical, mental, emotional and spiritual experience. Theoretically, these atmospheres are really all aspects of a single energy field which might radiate out from each of us into infinity. If this were true, it would mean that, just like individual atoms, each of us is interpenetrating or overlapping with everyone and everything else – a truly Universal Oneness.'

From the above it is clear that Harry believes we are all 'connected', that we are all One. Along these lines, he often points out the energy interactions that are occurring between people and their surroundings which are evident on PIP scans.

Once the clinic and school became established, many people started making their way there by referral. Others were intrigued by the positive reports they saw in the media about natural healing in general and electro-crystal therapy in particular.

Typical of these was one in a local newspaper, the *Evening Echo*, in February 1986. It carried a photograph of Harry administering electro-crystal therapy to a patient's ear. The caption read, 'Turning off the hum ... electro-crystal therapist Harry Oldfield treats Joan Tyler.'

The article told the story of a Basildon mother of three young children who had been driven to a nervous breakdown by tinnitus. She heard noises continuously, even at night, which prevented sleep. The best advice a hospital consultant could offer was to try and get to sleep with a radio playing by her bed. Not happy with this, Joan was one of six badly-affected Essex volunteers trying electro-crystal therapy. The trials were being financed by Whistlestop, the Basildon branch of the British Tinnitus Association.

'Whilst the patient felt a faint buzz, there are no side-effects and there is no possibility of doing any harm,' said Harry, who by that time had been offering electro-crystal therapy for about four years and had trained almost 50 other operators, including a Harley Street doctor.

After her second treatment Joan experienced two days of complete relief before her tinnitus returned. Following the third treatment she reported: 'I can hardly hear the noise at all and I feel really relaxed.'

Others taking part in the trial had not all had such positive results, though several said the noise was less intense.

The work continued both home and abroad. The latter part of June 1986 found Harry at the First International Crystal Congress in California. He met some interesting people at this event and, through these contacts, went on to demonstrate his techniques at a number of similar events around the world.

During his many talks, Harry spent a great deal of time explaining how the energy or 'life force' surrounding our bodies governs our health and well-being. He would carry out demonstrations on volunteers from the audience, scanning them and pointing out their health problems, past, present and even future with amazing accuracy and speed, and would then offer a short treatment.

Many people, after 10 to 15 minutes of treatment with electro-crystal therapy, reported being able to perform tasks they said they could not have attempted before. We have seen this ourselves a number of times. For example, someone with a bad back who could not touch their toes before treatment found that they could easily do so afterwards.

Asked how he felt about orthodox medical treatment at the time, Harry said:

'I don't like my work to be called "alternative". I call it "complementary", because I believe we complement each other. And I can certainly say that if I were ever injured in a car accident, I wouldn't want someone there with my equipment – I'd want an ambulance!

'As an organization, the health system in the UK is very conservative. I understand that it has to be this way for our own safety, especially with regard to new drugs being tested. This conservatism can slow down acceptance of new ideas but I must stress that I cannot think of any better support than I have received from doctors as individuals ... so much so that I now have a permanent medical consultant to our school.'

With all this interest and support it wasn't long before other therapists began to use Harry's therapy. He comments on this as follows:

'The beauty of electro-crystal therapy is that it can be used by practitioners of other complementary natural therapies to add both a scientific dimension and a degree of repeatability to the diagnosis and treatment of energy field imbalances. The machine is the same every time, whereas the human therapist is not.

'This is not of course to take anything away from individual practitioners who may have healing gifts which offer something very different from what is offered by my machines. What I am saying is that electro-crystal therapy can be an ideal complement to other therapies, based as it is so firmly in science.'

Meanwhile the equipment continued to evolve. In 1977, Harry had developed the first version of the electro-generator *(see plate section)*. Version One was essentially a prototype, built from a 'project box' and including bulky parts and handmade circuitry. 'Not exactly high-tech, but it did the job,' as Harry reflects today.

A few years later, in 1980, Version Two was developed. This was much more sophisticated, although it still relied on handmade circuitry.

Version Three was a real breakthrough. Electronic technology had moved on considerably in the early 1980s and by 1986 Harry was able to include integrated circuits on printed boards in the new much more powerful design. Technological developments also paved the way for the separate development of a portable machine – and, of course, the original Kirlian or 'electro-generator' was now called an 'electro-crystal generator', since the crystal chip electrode had now been in use for some time.

Version Four, the current model, was developed in the mid-1990s to comply with stricter regulations and safety standards imposed by European guidelines. Unlike the earlier versions, which were battery only, this is a mains-operated unit with battery back-up.

In 1987 Harry was also able to develop a generating machine which pulsed light frequencies through the crystals rather than sound and radio frequencies. By incorporating light emitting diode (LED) technology, he was able to demonstrate that light frequencies often had an even more beneficial effect than his other methods in certain skin or eye conditions. He called this 'opto-crystal therapy'.

This LED machine followed on from earlier experiments with lasers, which Harry had also found to have therapeutic effects. Before starting this opto-crystal research, Harry already knew that, in a crystal lattice, matter was in one of its most stable and balanced states but that it could be disturbed by contact with outside forces, thereby emitting energy which could be used therapeutically. When he went on to experiment with lasers, a cold helium neon laser was used to release energy from the crystal network. The therapeutic effect was achieved both by direct contact of the crystal on the skin and by 'projection', whereby coherent laser light was passed through the crystals, producing interference patterns which were then played onto the patient's body.

Harry expands:

'Radiant light energy is propagated in the form of electro-magnetic waves. Light of a particular controlled frequency is described as monochromatic light. We used monochromatic red light because of the element used in its generation, which was neon. It is light of this nature – with every particle, call them phota if you must, beating in resonance – which makes laser apparatus function.

'Since all these phota are in step with one another, they tend not to diffuse like an ordinary beam of light. They can be thought of as a single thin ray of light which does not spread out.'

On his courses, Harry describes the laser light as orderly soldiers marching out of a fort while normal light, which spreads out all over the place, is a football crowd emerging from a stadium. He continues:

'When a laser light source is shone through a crystal, the light undergoes refraction and sometimes reflection off imperfect lattices and inclusions and so on. However, unlike ordinary light, which after this process would spread out or diverge, the laser light passing through the crystal remains coherent, even though it may be refracted or reflected and split into several beams.

'Therefore, any split light forms an interesting pattern due to the individual structure of the crystal itself. Since the equilibrium of the crystal is also disturbed, when this pattern is played on a part of the body which responds and vibrates sympathetically with the healing aspect of the crystal, interesting therapeutic results are seen. As these split beams travel away from the crystal they fan out or diverge to a certain small degree but without the information of the pattern being lost.'

Harry learned a lot about light and crystals from the laser experiments. The main reason he chose not to incorporate laser light into his opto-crystal therapy system was the safety factor, because certain lasers can irretrievably harm the eyes. However, the knowledge gained from the laser experiments was very pertinent to the entirely safe LED-based system which is now in use.

Opto-crystal therapy uses light pulsed through crystals to much greater benefit than could be achieved by merely pulsing the same light without the crystals. 'The optical unit,' says Harry, 'has the therapeutic advantages of laser light but uses light-emitting diodes which present no danger to the eyes.'

Originally the colour of the light was red – due to availability of diodes – but, as you will see from the plate section, the spectrum of colour rays used has now expanded to include blue and violet. Harry envisions further colours becoming available in the future but can only speculate on the relative therapeutic advantages until he has had a chance to test the effect of each different colour on the energy field.

Harry wanted to maintain the same pulse rates for the opto-crystal generator as for the electro-crystal one, but:

'The frequencies were, by definition, higher because light frequencies are higher up the electromagnetic spectrum than sound and radio frequencies.

'The opto-crystal model has enhanced the therapeutic results with certain conditions considerably – in cases of eczema, psoriasis and scar tissue, for example, and also glaucoma, conjunctivitis and long- or short-sightedness.'

Harry is a good example of his own treatment. He is a crack shot who used to need glasses just to see the target. After six months of opto-crystal therapy, he was able to clearly see the target without his glasses. Many others have reported similar remarkable improvements in both long- and short-sightedness.

Yet another development is crystal sound therapy, in which sound is generated from crystals and used to therapeutic effect. This process uses highly tuned electromagnetic waves to excite individual crystals to such a high level that they begin to emit audible sound waves; each crystal seems to have a loud individual note at which it resonates, that is, vibrates and gives off sound energy. Harry says:

'The rule is that the larger the crystal, the lower the frequency, and the smaller the crystal, the higher the frequency.

'One might reasonably ask whether, apart from an interesting noise, any other use can be obtained from such an exercise. On the one hand, we could say that pure research for its own sake needs no justification as long as it is interesting. On the other, the sound itself has had a therapeutic effect on many who have heard it, depending on the attributes of the crystal being used.

'Even deaf people, or people with hearing difficulties, have received benefit, proving that the vibrations which have been set up are bringing about an effect in the body and are not simply the physical sound at audible frequencies.'

Interestingly, a crystal sound CD – referred to by all involved as 'Harry and the Crystals' – was later made with rock group

Current '93. When it was released in California, this CD sold out all its 10,000 copies in a very short time.

Whilst the crystal sounds were being recorded in the studio, some unusual phenomena were witnessed, such as speakers mysteriously falling off walls.

On a positive therapeutic note, a couple of the technicians did notice an improvement in their health. One, who was experiencing a bad bout of asthma, was amazed to find that it abated during the session and remained better for quite a while afterwards.

Harry expands:

'The features of this crystal sound method are, first, that the treatment is non-invasive; second, that a variety of crystals with different properties can be used; and third, that groups of people can be treated at the same time.'

Harry even found that gloomy living and working environments changed for the better when crystal sounds were generated into them, though he qualifies this somewhat:

'This last statement is, of course, a subjective one, but when we are dealing with subtle energies such as these, some subjectivity might reasonably be included.

'Only time and more research on people and places will give any positive answers as to the effectiveness of this variation on electro-crystal therapy. But there is good reason to be optimistic. After all, it seems to be an extension to the well-known soothing effects of good music, which necessarily produces harmonic frequencies.'

The other side of the coin is Harry's belief that disease itself could be spread by a sort of radio message from one person to another. This would explain things like the 'flu 'viruses' which can break out in many places at the same time without direct transmission from one person to another. This is also why Harry feels that broadcasting the correct transmissions can be so beneficial in achieving and maintaining health.

As he asks, 'And can you imagine the effect if we had 10 million of these healing machines all broadcasting in unison in people's homes around the world?'

During July 1987 Harry was once again in the United States promoting his work. The International Institute of Creative Sciences had invited him back to California State University. The theme of the conference was 'Electro-Crystal Applications and Conscious Transformation through Light, Colour and Sound'.

Then in November 1987, the Thames TV morning programme *After Nine Special* featured Harry's work. Jayne Irving interviewed Harry and he treated a member of the studio staff who had injured her leg on the way to work that morning. After 10 minutes' treatment she reported an improvement, apparently much to the surprise of the interviewer!

This was a busy time for Harry. Another trip to North America followed. Late November found him a guest speaker at a conference called 'Electro-Crystal Applications' at the Relax Inn, Mississauga, Ontario, Canada. Once again he amazed the audience with his diagnostic and treatment demonstration.

In between these events, Harry still found time to treat patients at his clinic. A typical day at the clinic generally reveals an array of complaints being treated. One day we arrived to find in one room a person with cancer receiving treatment to boost her immune system, while in another room someone with a frozen shoulder was gaining relief and in yet another a woman with stress was wearing a visor which was pulsing soothing lights onto her brow chakra. She told us she felt 'very calm for many days after each treatment'.

In Harry's office was another lady. After asking permission, Harry explained her case:

'When Sheila first came to see me she was on the waiting list for a heart-lung transplant and the scan I gave her looked very bad. However, we decided that what God gave we should keep, and within six months of our starting the treatment the hospital took her off the danger list and she has recently had a hospital check which has given her the all clear.

'When she first came the problem was in the energy field – a blockage of the chakras, primarily of the heart centre, which had a direct effect on her physical heart and lungs. There was attenuation of the solar plexus and a problem with her throat centre. There was also energy depletion in the base centre, which gave her circulatory problems and cold feet, but this was a separate problem which had come long before the heart-lung problem.

'We see the chakras as the energetic assembly points for these major organ centres and when there is a problem with the blueprint the physical structure suffers.

'Our main work is energy restructuring. We are like a general energy-medicine practice and we can help with anything that affects the mind-body interrelationship because we work on the causal energy field, which is the causative factor of the energy patterns of the body.'

Sheila says she has improved considerably due to electro-crystal therapy. She tells her own story in Chapter 7.

There are two parts to Harry's therapy: diagnosis and treatment using 'natural energy'. Having looked at Harry's early diagnostic work and how this came to develop into treatment, we can now move on to look in more detail at the development of another diagnostic method: polycontrast interference photography, otherwise known as the PIP scanning system. Let us briefly recap to put this discovery in context.

In his search for a way to measure those elusive morphogenetic fields, Harry had started looking into Kirlian photography.

With this technique he could achieve two-dimensional pictures of the energy field but the process also produced undesirable 'artefacts' and required darkroom conditions.

From there he had progressed to the Kirlian gun, which offered three-dimensional quantitive scans by turning the human being into a 'radio beacon' and 'hearing' the energy field in ordinary daylight clinical conditions. This worked much like sonar by putting signals in to get a usable measurement out and also had far fewer artefacts. However, the oscilloscope used with the Kirlian gun was somewhat cumbersome for demonstrations and beyond the pocket of the average person. Harry therefore came up with the electro-scanning method, or ESM.

As he explains, both the Kirlian gun and ESM measured quantitative changes in the energy field by analysing energetic emanations from the body produced by contact with one of Harry's Kirlian or electro-crystal generators:

'These emanations were approximately 70 per cent electromagnetic or radio frequencies and 30 per cent sound frequencies, hence they could be picked up on an oscilloscope, a pen-chart recorder or with a radio-sound level meter. The radio-sound level meter offered many practical benefits.

'However, in changing the way I got the information, I lost the startling visual or qualitative images and had to make do visually with oscilloscope patterns, or needle fluctuations in the case of the radio-sound meter. Although these other methods had advantages, I was quite disappointed to have lost the visual aspect and this was always in the back of my mind.'

By the early 1980s, Harry had developed a therapy which pulsed high-frequency electromagnetic energy through crystals in saline solution in an attempt to tune and rebalance the human energetic system. Over the course of the next decade he was able to refine this therapy and gain a great deal of clinical experience both in diagnosis and treatment. But, as is the way of things, this therapy was also a stepping-stone to further new ideas. During 1988, Harry met a man on a trip to America who would send him off in a new direction yet again.

Dr Richard Gerber is a medical doctor who studied energy in relation to medicine for 12 years before publishing what is considered by many to be a 'must read' textbook on the subject: *Vibrational Medicine: New Choices for Healing Ourselves* (Bear and Co, 1988).

Harry met Dr Gerber while on a lecture tour in North America and it was he who suggested to Harry that he might apply the new technology of the micro-chip computer to his energy-field scanning techniques in order to make a scanner which could provide a real-time moving image of the energy field.

'I'm going to write about what you are doing in my book,' said Dr Gerber, 'and will end by saying that I believe that the future of diagnosis lies in finding an effective scanner which can "see" disease in the energy field rather than the physical body. This is what I'm going to write. If you want to accept the challenge and be first, that's up to you. Otherwise, someone else will have to do it.' True to his word, Dr Gerber did write a significant section about Harry's work in his book.

Harry's first response was to reply that he would love to have the financial resources to develop this idea, but he was working in his garden shed! However, as usual, he put his thinking cap on and just got on with it.

By the following year he had come up with the first prototype PIP scanner, a system that could offer a qualitative real-time three-dimensional moving image of the energy field.

Nine years later, it has progressed a great deal and hardware can be attached and software loaded onto any IBM-compatible computer using either Windows 3.1 or '95. This world-wide user-friendliness is an intentionally built-in feature. Harry is always trying to keep his systems inexpensive so that more people can have access to them. In fact he says that it was mainly due to his own very limited resources that he had to come up with such a financially viable and practical solution.

Harry's dream is that these scanners will become common-place in both orthodox and complementary medical centres around the world:

> 'Any clinic with a computer could have one. Of course, analysis of the information, pattern recognition and so on is a completely different matter. Whilst anyone could look at an X-ray of a broken leg, gaining useful clinical information from it is something which requires specialist training, knowledge and experience. The same is true with using PIP.'

Getting back to Harry's original thinking in regard to PIP, he wondered whether the human energy field might possibly inter-fere with photons – 'energy packets' of light – or even what might be called 'subtle energy photons' in some way. He decided that ambient (surrounding) light would be interfered with by the field both when the incident ray travelled towards the object and when the reflected ray bounced off the object (in the main, the 'object' being human beings).

First of all, Harry needed an artificial eye which would provide a constantly updated image, just as the human eye does. He explains:

> 'The human eye has to make very small movements all the time for the purpose of tracking and depth perception, both because the optic nerve exits from the eye at the "blind spot" and because the very nature of neural stimulation is such that unless an image is refreshed, its excitation will stop having an effect.'

This artificial eye was easy to find in the form of an ordinary video camera (which constantly updates and refreshes an image electromagnetically).

Next Harry would need an artificial brain which could make some sense of the signals from the artificial eye/video camera. He had already discussed this with Dr Gerber and the artificial brain took the form of an ordinary micro-chip computer. Then an ordinary insulated wire lead between the camera/eye and computer/brain became the artificial optic nerve.

The next piece of the puzzle would prove to be the really clever bit. Harry had to do the mathematics which would form the basis of the computer programme which would have to analyse the many different light intensities that any ordinary video camera can 'see' in the form of reflected rays from the object/person being filmed or, in this case, 'scanned'. The computer programme would have to compare the reflected rays with the incident rays and then produce an image which made some sense of the process for the human observer.

Harry had some idea of the image that might be produced based on his own research, that of other scientists and the subjective reports of ancient and modern 'sensitives' who reported the colours, lines and patterns of the energy field. Having developed his theories, he enlisted the help of a brilliant young computer programmer, John Catchpole. John converted Harry's ideas into computer-recognizable language and the resulting programme runs the PIP system.

Harry explained:

'Imagine a bar code on a supermarket can. The video camera and computer are used in the PIP system to scan a person in a same way that the supermarket checkout machine scans the bar code.

'Our system comes up with a set of numbers from the scan by giving photons a number. It is a digital encoding system. The minutest change in density of photons is recorded and amplified to give the picture you see on the computer screen. We scan at 50 frames per second, so this is a lot of information processing.'

This system is both deceptively simple and enormously accurate in the hands of people who know both how to operate it and what they are looking at. It is, of course, a lot less useful to people who would not know a chakra from a cell or a meridian from a muscle. At the present time fewer than 25 people are competent operators of the system, but this will obviously change as more people become aware of PIP and are trained in its usage.

Harry is often asked whether the colours seen with PIP are the actual colours of the aura. He told us:

'Absolutely. What we're trying to observe with PIP is a kind of interference pattern. The theory is based on the fact that our eyes see in two ways. Partly we see in amplitude changes – dark light gives small amplitude changes whereas bright light gives larger ones. We also see in colour, which is represented by frequency changes. We see the longer wavelengths as red and the shorter as violet.

'Also, there are phase changes and interference takes place between the wave patterns. And if you've got a natural emitting energy body, like the human body – we are a complex mix of mind, body and spirit and are therefore giving off a lot of energies – then it will interact with surrounding light energy and produce interference patterns and colours. These patterns and colours are what I believe clairvoyants and mystics see. They naturally have eye and brain mechanisms that can pick up these subtle changes of light.

'When you're looking at chakra colours on our visual equipment, you're not just seeing one colour, you're seeing a mixture of colours. But if a chakra is behaving itself perfectly, one colour will predominate – for instance the throat chakra has more of a blue hue when it's healthy than when it's not. The same with the base chakra – it will be a dirty muddy brown if there are problems and red if it's healthy. Also when red kundalini energy goes elsewhere, that is, goes into the wrong place at the wrong time, there is a potential danger. I am able to show this to people when they come for a PIP scan. I see particularly dangerous distortions in people with diseases such as MS and cancer.'

Harry has spent many years studying cancer. We asked him to expand on his findings in this area:

'Apart from seeing, in most cases, an attenuated energy pattern or blockage in the relevant area or the thymus gland, which is important to the immune system, I often detect low energy states compounded by stress. I often see severe energy blockages which damn the flow of the life-force at certain key points around the body. I may even see the life force leaking away from the body atmosphere and into the surrounding environment. This phenomenon may be similar to what Tesla called a "streamer".

'The tumour sites, if active, are often seen as distinct red energy configurations in the "wrong" area. In high activity we often see white spots which are indications of high frequency patterns due to rapid cell division.

'Since each colour represents a particular frequency of energy, a cancer tumour often shows up as a high intensity energy spot which is not connected with a chakra or meridian. These are usually rounded in shape, although they can be elliptical or undifferentiated.

'But there are a lot of other factors which contribute to the diagnosis of something seriously pathological. For example, toxic signals from the liver and distortions over the thymus gland could indicate that the immune system is involved. There are many other visual clues.

'As cancer can be thought of as a rapid division of "rogue" cells which the body's police force, the immune system, is unable to control, the over-activity of the cells would be expected to cause a corresponding convex "bump" in the energy field, at or near the site of the tumour. You will notice from the bladder tumour PIP image side view [see plate section] that this is exactly what appears to be happening. You will also notice the red lines of congestion in the energy field all down the front of the man's body.

'If we were to use the electro-scanning method in the case of this bladder tumour, we might get a reading of "plus 3" or "plus 4" relative to the normal site (which would read "0") in the area of the bulge. My theory is that the bulge in the picture and the plus reading during ESM may be due to the activity of rapidly dividing cells.

'Electro-crystal therapy seeks to quieten the "rebellion" and restore order and calm. When order is restored, another PIP image would hopefully provide evidence of this to the concerned patient by showing a much reduced bulge amongst other changes in this *qualitative* scanning system. With regard to the *quantitative* analysis of the energy field using ESM, after therapy we would hope to see a reduction in the plus reading towards the balance of zero.'

Harry has found being able to show before and after PIP images and ESM readings is of great comfort to those who seek his help.

As we have already mentioned, with its ability to detect disturbances in the energy field prior to physical symptoms manifesting, PIP could play a part in preventative medicine.

In this regard, we PIP scanned one lady who had significantly congested energy patterns over her left hip area as well as over a portion of her left lower jaw.

We pointed this out to her and she said that she had no problems in those areas. The day after the PIP she went on holiday – and was unfortunately plagued by toothache (left lower jaw) and by pain in her left hip! When she next came to see us she said that her holiday 'wasn't as wonderful as it could have been ... I had to have a lot of dental treatment and take quite a few painkillers. But having said this, I'm very impressed with the PIP system which predicted these problems.'

Some would argue that this episode was due to auto-suggestion. This is a valid point, but there have been numerous cases where PIP scans have shown blocked energy manifesting in an area in which a physical problem later becomes apparent. In other words, the PIP seems to be able to highlight areas of potential debility.

Harry regularly performs a series of PIP scans over months or even years in order to assess changes in a person's energy body. For example, someone may have problems with digestion. This may manifest on PIP as congested energy in the solar plexus area. In addition the chakra may be seen to be misshapen or constricted. After treatment or a change of lifestyle and diet the energy field can be monitored to assess progress (along with changes in symptoms and test results).

During a normal PIP scanning session about five still images of the moving scan are captured. Ordinarily these would be of the front, back, side, head and legs of the person so that the PIP practitioner can obtain an overview of the person's energy field. These still images form the basis of the energy field diagnostic report that is provided to the patient.

At the time of writing (1998) the latest development is that a few minutes of video footage can be provided for people to take away rather than still images. But on this point Harry reminds us:

'Of course, the energy field is in a continual state of change. All sorts of things can influence it, from how much you had to drink last night to whether you have been in a smoky atmosphere at work. PIP practitioners have to learn how to incorporate these factors into their energy field diagnosis.'

Emotional factors can also play a part. We asked Harry about his experience with emotional and psychological conditions. He said:

'First we must link the physical with the other aspects of the human being.

'The body is an empire of billions of cells with an energy system that assists in keeping them all in the right place doing what they are supposed to. This empire of cells and energies is ruled by the brain.

'On a physical or mechanical level, the brain uses chemical messengers called hormones to regulate the various systems in the body. The pituitary or master gland – which controls the function of the other glands – is located in the brain.

'On an energy level the brain is a transceiver which constantly transmits and receives information to and from the physical and energy systems of the body. When we are healthy this is evidence that the brain is able to keep the physical and energy systems in the body in a state of homoeostasis and balance. When we are unhealthy the brain is failing to do this.

'In this way, influences on the brain, such as stress and electromagnetic pollution, cause a *disorganizing* effect on the energy field, thus upsetting both the energetic balance and physical homoeostasis.

'Until very recently it was thought that visualization and other such mind/brain techniques could not work, because the mind lacks the power to intervene in a physical disease like cancer. This belief is now being disputed. Neurochemists have been unravelling the processes by which suggestion and autosuggestion transmit their messages, and they have shown that mind power has reserves capable of altering the body's chemistry. I feel there are huge advances to be made in the treatment of many conditions once we understand more about the myriad of body/brain/mind/subtle energy interactions.

'Some of us may spend our whole lifetime trying to cope with our emotions and life in general. In this respect, electro-crystal therapy seems to hold some sort of key to unlocking and opening doors that would otherwise remain closed. It is my experience that many people start to find answers inside themselves after treatment. This is something they were innately capable of doing but just seemed to need some help with.

'We are dealing here with very subtle changes in a person's life-force energy. The slightest tweak can often work where more direct approaches fail.'

It is a central theme of energy medicine that the chakras, or energy centres, are a link between the physical, mental, emotional and spiritual energy 'bodies'. These bodies are not necessarily to be understood as separate and distinct; they are more likely to be different aspects of a single energy field for each person.

If this is the case, it is not at all surprising that Harry often finds an emotional or psychological improvement in a person when, say, treating the heart chakra for a physical condition. This would indeed indicate that there might be a subtle link between the different layers of the energy field.

That link may be the whirlpool shape and motion of the chakras, which enables the postulated 'astral waters' or 'subtle life-energies' to flow around the system and thus integrate the physical, mental, emotional and spiritual aspects of the total human experience.

Another suggestion is that all the energy bodies of everything in the universe overlap, interpenetrate and interact with each other, so, as Harry as already mentioned, we may all be integrating continuously within One Universal Whole.

Harry says, 'Just like water droplets in a sea, in the invisible universe of subtle energies it is hard to see where a droplet ends and the ocean begins.'

In 1991, the obituary column in the 7 November issue of the *Herts and Essex Observer* gave the name of a patient whom the Oldfields had helped. The man's wife thanked 'Mr and Mrs Harry Oldfield and Mrs A. Catchpole of The School of Electro-Crystal Therapy who gave hope, comfort and 15 months for which I am eternally grateful'. We asked Harry how he copes with trying to help so many seriously ill people. He replied:

'I feel that if a person has been guided towards me for help, my purpose is to help them as much as I can. What I can do is to try to improve the quality of life of that person. If they are in pain or suffering, or if they have mental anguish, I can usually do something to relieve them of that – or, rather than me, the good Lord who commanded me to. Having said this, I can only do my best and would never give false hope to anybody who was meant to die.'

Certainly electro-crystal therapy does not help everyone. In Harry's experience there has always been a proportion of people who have not benefited from the treatment. He comments on this:

'Although the majority of people are helped in some way with the frequencies which are delivered via the crystals, there are those who show no improvement. It could be that the electromagnetic frequencies are not in the required range for these people.

'I have even had people come for treatment and feel a remarkable benefit for some of their health problems but not for others. There are numerous reasons why a therapy doesn't work, for example denial, emotional issues and resistance to treatment.

'Often counselling on lifestyle may be of benefit or perhaps emotional problems may need to be explored before healing can take place. Each individual is a complex, integrated system. It would be too simplistic an approach to treat them all the same. We assess each person who comes to us individually and holistically.

'Sometimes treatment helps release emotional blocks. Patients have often reported back to me that after a treatment session with electro-crystal therapy they have gone home feeling relaxed and have had an emotional release, often about something which happened years before.

'A great number of people who come for treatment are having other complementary therapies at the same time.

After treatment with electro-crystal therapy many acupuncturists and reflexologists, when assessing energy flow and foot reflex points, have reported improvements in the areas which had been treated with electro-crystal therapy.

'Many of our therapists practise other therapies. Let me give you an example. One is a chiropractor. He finds that, when treating back problems, a short anti-inflammatory treatment with electro-crystal therapy over an area of muscle spasm will help relax the muscles sufficiently so that he can perform his manipulations, often much sooner than would normally be the case.

'As electro-crystal therapy aims to balance the body's subtle fields and promote healing, its therapeutic benefits can be helped considerably if the person attempts to extend this balancing to all areas of their lives.

'Too often we take no notice of our body complaining that it cannot cope with the pace. How many of us see a tension headache as an inconvenience which makes us only stop long enough to swallow a painkiller? Heaven forbid that it should stop us from burning the candle at both ends again tonight! Likewise, all too frequently indigestion is just a nuisance that stops us from enjoying the fried food and Indian take-aways which we love so much.

'We are all guilty of neglecting our body and ignoring its needs. Sometimes we need help in getting ourselves back in balance. This is where my machines can help. But of course we need to help ourselves too. Balance between work, rest and play, and eating a balanced diet can enhance well-being on their own. When coupled with an energy-balancing therapy a synergistic response is often achieved.'

We can now make some general points about Harry's therapeutic techniques as they have developed over the years.

A very interesting feature of ESM was that Harry had not been using it for long as a diagnostic device before patients began to tell him that they seemed to feel better afterwards. They would ask for further appointments – for ESM therapy.

Donald McCormick, an author who also writes under the name Richard Deacon, was suffering from arthritic pains in his joints. He noted a 'marked difference' after his first ESM session and after three sessions there was a substantial improvement. His wife Eileen was equally impressed. She had suffered four years of discomfort following a hiatus hernia operation, but after three visits to Harry declared: 'It has eased a lot, and I feel generally stronger and less tired.'

Sharon Saatchi, a beautician, had experienced painful muscular spasms in the back for several years following a diving accident. After ESM therapy her opinion was that her condition was 'much better'.

Other patients also reported improvements – sometimes occurring immediately – in a number of conditions ranging from sinusitis, high blood pressure and headaches to general feelings of being unwell.

One of the Oldfields' most satisfied early patients may have been Sharon Saatchi's dog. For some time it had been dragging a hind leg in evident pain, but after a single ESM session, which it seemed to enjoy, it scampered around the room with no sign of a limp.

This pointed the way towards a number of vets successfully incorporating electro-crystal therapy into their practices. Working with animals had another advantage for the research too – that favourite charge of the detractors, the 'placebo effect', could be ruled out completely. Many animals, birds, fish and even plants have since benefited from Harry's treatment.

Harry has often been asked about the contribution made by heat to his diagnostic and treatment techniques. He comments:

'In the 1890s the French doctor Arsène d'Arsonval employed alternating currents oscillating at very high frequencies. He believed such high-frequency currents had general therapeutic value and this was the forerunner of what is now called "diathermy" – the induction of "deep heat" in body tissues by radio-frequency currents, microwaves or ultrasound.

'A New York doctor, Abraham Ginsberg, is the man usually credited with the introduction of pulsed high-frequency electro-therapy (which has no heating effect). This has been used, many would say successfully, since 1934, for treating wounds, muscular disorders, rheumatoid arthritis, sprains and even broken bones. Practitioners claim that the technique helps damaged cells to heal themselves.

'Over the years it has been discovered that cells appear to be sensitive to certain very precise frequencies, pulse repetition rates and current strengths. These are known as "windows".

'These various techniques are basically the same as mine, though we think we have developed the fine tuning considerably, especially using the crystals. It is important to note here that no heat is induced by my electro-crystal therapy techniques and, of course, the PIP system does not measure heat but rather the interaction of light and the energy field.

'It seems that we have found a way of increasing the number of "windows" of healing opportunity which can be opened with the crystal-filled electrode, the tuning fork which vibrates the energy and thus encourages the cells back into a state of balance.

'And, what is more, these pulsed high-frequency energies are very safe. As Dr Robert Becker puts it: "If you exceed the range, the cell will just sit and do nothing." The way I explain it is that it's like ringing the wrong telephone number – you just don't get through. But even if communication is not possible, neither the telephone nor the intended recipient of the call is harmed by the failure to get connected.'

Over the years, there has been a great deal of media coverage of Harry's work from both near and far.

In Harry's local newspaper in November 1988 the case of his next-door neighbour was reported under the heading: 'Harry the miracle worker'.

In 1976, doctors had told Ruislip carpenter Ted Thrumble that he would never use his left hand again. It was completely paralysed following an accident. But even though Ted had lived next door to Harry for several years, he did not try his neighbour's treatment until he realized that conventional medicine had no more to offer him.

To his surprise, after a period of treatment Ted was able to wriggle his fingers, grip a hammer and go back to the carpentry job he loved.

'You can see how badly damaged it was,' he says, showing a hand riddled with scars. 'Now it's working properly – I can even feel a splinter going in. It's a miracle.'

In contrast, Harry's work was also covered as far away as Australia, in an article in the 10 January 1990 issue of the *Gold Coast Bulletin*. Under the title 'New therapy helps body repair itself', readers were told that Runaway Bay resident Hazel Hill practised electro-crystal therapy. Hazel said:

'I have used the therapy to treat babies through to old people – I have even used it on animals and plants. One patient was a 10-year-old Old English sheepdog. Her mammary glands had been removed and the vet said she would not live long. Her owners brought her to me and I treated her. There was a definite improvement within a week and within months her coat had grown back and she was chasing rabbits.

'If one of my plants looks sick, I'll put a vibration through them. My daughter burnt her hand on a hot plate months ago and I put the electrode on it. The next morning you couldn't see anything – it didn't even blister.'

Hazel went to Australia as a pioneer of electro-crystal therapy. She says:

'It's an international therapy but there are only a handful of people in Australia who practise it. It has been accepted overseas so I'm sure it will be accepted here. The only way I can prove the therapy is if people come and experience it. Everyone can benefit because no one is completely healthy.

'I think there's a lot I can do with skin cancers too. Sometimes the therapy can abort the need for an operation – it depends on how far the disease has progressed. However, I must emphasize that electro-crystal therapy does not take the place of medical diagnosis and co-operation with a medical practitioner would be highly favoured. I would like to work with doctors, but I don't know what their attitudes will be.'

Back at home, in the spring of 1990, *Kindred Spirit* magazine (Vol.1, no.10) reported on the potential of Harry Oldfield's work and showed some graphic PIP photographs of the energy body before and after electro-crystal therapy. (A number of other people are currently researching PIP's capability to show before, during and after images of other therapies such as reflexology, acupuncture and healing.)

Richard Beaumont, the editor, had heard about Harry's work with Kirlian photography, but was certainly not expecting what he found at Harry's clinic: 'Patients abounded, he was treating them in the living room, in the kitchen, the bedrooms, it seemed that every room was full of people awaiting his attentions, and more appeared as the day went on.'

With regard to the current research going on to analyse changes in the energy field when certain techniques are applied, two PIP images taken before and during hands-on healing therapy can be seen in the plate section. The subject remained in the same position and all other conditions such as lighting and camera were consistent. The only change was the healing practitioners entering the subject's energy field a few seconds after the first image was captured.

In the 'before' image we believe the red and magenta lines and patches show areas of congestion and turbulence in the energy field, that is, where the energy is not flowing as it would in a well-balanced field. These patterns are generally present in areas of disease or trauma.

In this person's PIP scan we can see significant red/magenta imbalances in certain areas which relate to the existing physical condition of the person. These are over the throat (thyroid disease), pancreas (diabetes), liver (high alcohol consumption) and right arm (muscle strain).

The person was given immediate hands-on healing therapy. As the two practitioners entered his field, two white lights descended and the whole body went towards the more balanced colours of green and yellow. Perhaps most interestingly, the solar plexus (or 'sun') chakra seemed to burst open with yellow light. The base chakra, too, appeared to be energized, as evidenced by the boxer shorts turning red.

Another possibility as to why the red energy seems to have disappeared from the torso and appeared in the base chakra is that the energy may have been leaving the body by 'earthing', perhaps due to the healing. This, however, is pure speculation.

Whether you agree with these interpretations of the images or not, it is difficult to deny that dramatic changes occurred. *Something* is happening that is invisible to normal sight.

The potential for this comparative application in orthodox and complementary medicine is enormous. One day, we will hopefully be able to see the effects of all therapies, treatments and techniques on the human energy field.

However, with such new technology and the ideas which Harry has postulated, it is inevitable that there will be differing views amongst the 'experts' as to what PIP actually shows and how useful it is. Recently, when the science editor of a well-known magazine was shown some of Harry's PIP pictures, he summarily dismissed the whole process and all the results as 'nothing but penumbral shadows'. This form of predisposition is perhaps impossible to deal with.

Given the doubters, we asked Harry about his ability to scan people with his machines and come up with such accurate diagnoses in a few minutes. We reminded him that others had said that it was not the machines but his own intuitive ability that was enabling such apparently impossible feats. Harry said:

'Over 20 years I have become "sensitive" to people's state of dis-ease, but only in the same way that a physician becomes sensitive to the "presenting symptoms" of his patients. Lots of knowledge, combined with experience, may give an impression of sensitivity which I wouldn't necessarily deny but would moderate with that comment.

'It might be useful to think of Sherlock Holmes and Watson. Holmes used to amaze Watson by saying something like, "Watson, that man has had fried eggs for breakfast." What the sleuth saw that Watson didn't was the fresh yolk stains on the man's tie. So it is with what I do. Yes, it is sensitivity of observational skill, experience of what to look for plus a knowledge of subtle energy and anatomy and how they are affected in disease – but anyone could learn it.'

Throughout the 1990s, Harry has continued to attract national media attention, with coverage in the *Independent* (Saturday 11 February 1995) and the *Daily Mail* (Saturday 11 March 1995), as well as in many other newspapers, magazines and journals. This all points to the probability that electro-crystal therapy will grow and grow as we move towards 2000 and beyond.

We asked Harry if he had any particularly remarkable memories from all the healing successes with his techniques:

'Well, any person who benefits in any small way is always satisfying and as you know there have been lots of cases where we could point to improvements. But one young lady from Israel sticks in my mind. She was diagnosed as paraplegic and the doctors said she would certainly never walk again. She had a tumour on the spine. We were able to help her with electro-crystal therapy and I was able to see a video of taking her first steps a short while ago, although she had been told that she would be in that wheelchair forever.'

'What were you able to do for her?'

'I was able to focus the crystal energy field on the damaged area and somehow we jump-started her legs. She's a young person and young people in any injury seem to snap back more quickly.

'That's just one example of a paraplegic. I've also been able to help a young man who was left quadriplegic after an accident but who is now walking around – with a stick, but walking – and is a commercial artist with a great future ahead of him.'

At this point Harry rummages in a cupboard and pulls out a book to show us the inscription. The book is a gift from Mark, the commercial artist:

'To Harry, Eileen and Tony. Somewhere inside are words to describe everything, except how grateful I am to you.'

Obviously there have been many special people and special moments for Harry in the course of his work. He admitted:

'I've got a lot of faces passing in front of me going back over many, many years, but I think the greatest reward that I've had is simply to know some of my patients, especially those who knew they weren't going to recover, just to experience their company, and their bravery, and their faith in God, whichever creed they followed. Those who were the most ill were often the ones to have the most profound effect on me.

'That's helped to increase my own faith in our Lord because getting in company with people of that kind of faith, who are about to take the great plunge, the great journey into the unknown, the greatest journey that any man or woman can take, and to do it without resentment and regret and to go off in a such a serene way, to have helped them do that through gentle and natural means is a wonderful experience.

'Perhaps, in the orthodox medical view, such people would be looked upon as treatment failures, because they died. But to me the manner of our passing is important too. If I can help people to go out gently, with reduced pain and in a more positive frame of mind, then perhaps there is some measure of success inherent in that.

'And, ultimately, if what you are offering is care and compassion as well as a treatment that can work, people will vote with their feet and it's as simple as that.'

'Given the frustrations of the wilderness years, the lack of resources and so on, did you ever have doubts about what you were doing?'

'I think we all have doubts about many aspects of what we are doing at different points in our lives. But if I have any doubts now and then, all I have to do is look around my own house at all the carpentry work. It was all done by a carpenter whose hand became paralysed after an accident – and we restored it with our little pulsing energy machine against all the medical predictions.'

At this point Harry rose from his chair, tears beginning to well up in his eyes. Pointing out of the window, he told us:

'Look, he built my laboratory free of charge, down at the end of the garden, as a way of thanking us. That's the sort of people who come here – and it's been my privilege to know them.'

PERSPECTIVES

'One of the most striking features of the world is that its laws seem simple whilst the plethora of states and situations it manifests are extraordinarily complicated.'

JOHN D. BARROW

A WIDE variety of people meet and deal with Harry Oldfield on a weekly basis. Doctors, scientists, journalists, co-researchers and others all have intriguing stories to tell. Many ordinary people have been helped by Harry's therapy. We could not include all of their stories but there follows a selection.

THORNTON STREETER

Electro-Crystal Therapist (India)

Thornton Streeter is a Briton who actively promotes Harry's work around the world. We met Thornton at Harry's clinic in 1997. He talks about the unusual circumstances under which he met Harry and his experiences since.

'I was persuaded of the merits of Kirlian photography in India by a man they called "the Flying Swami". He was a guru and had earned that name from a famous incident, back in the 1960s, when he flew over East Germany and bombed them ... with flowers!

'I live and work in India and was invited to attend a Vedic [religious] ceremony. I was drawn to the work of Rosemary Steele, who was displaying Kirlian photography at the event. She and her equipment had been taken there by a group of NASA scientists who were investigating the phenomenon of "out-of-body experiences". They even brought Sanskrit scholars from Berkeley to help. It's a 26-day ceremony, held every 21 years. The chief priest is said to leave his body for a number of days and the NASA team wanted to test his Kirlian readings.

'When the priest had left his body, the Kirlian hand-print showed very much less energy than when he was in his "normal" waking or sleeping state.

'The Flying Swami was generally helping out with the organizing and for some reason he told me that I should take a serious look at Kirlian photography. I had come across it in journals, of course, as it was quite prominent at the time.

'When I was in England in 1990 I looked up "Kirlian" in the telephone directory at the library and found "Kirlian Research Institute". I phoned the number.

'Eileen answered and told me how Harry's work had progressed from the early Kirlian techniques. I was very keen to get on an electro-crystal therapy training course and arranged to attend one.

'Meanwhile, I went to California. I dived in the shallow end of a swimming-pool and hit the top of my head on the bottom, fracturing my spine in five places. I was told by the doctors that, in similar accidents, my neck would have been broken but for some reason I was very "fortunate" – if you can say that about having your spine fractured in five places and being very disabled by it!

'So, when I returned to England, I was a patient of Harry's first and a student second. Harry showed me how my crown chakra was "leaking" energy on the PIP scanner. I was amazed at how advanced this real-time energy field imaging system was when compared with the Kirlian equipment that the NASA team seemed to have had so much confidence in. Then, within no time at all, Harry had treated my crown chakra and spine with electro-crystal therapy and I had fully recovered. This made me doubly interested in learning to be an electro-crystal therapist.

'Now, seven years later, I've brought Dr Yamuna and her colleagues from India to do the advanced course with Harry. We are staying for three weeks and then they will be going back to concentrate on the clinic we've set up in Bombay. I've trained 35 people to foundation level so far in India. A great many are medical doctors.

'There is great interest in the scientific aspects of energy medicine in a country like India. I think it's because they've been using "natural" energy medicine for so long. You can imagine the stir we're causing now it appears that a Western-style scientific rationale can be applied to traditional Ayurvedic ideas. This is the best of both worlds for the doctors: natural principles with a rational scientific basis.'

DR K. S. YAMUNA

Medical Doctor and Electro-Crystal Therapist

We asked Dr Yamuna if she would care to contribute to this book. She readily agreed.

'I am a qualified medical doctor specializing in anaesthesia. Some time ago, after beginning to see the energy field or aura with my own eyes, I became very interested in energy medicine of all kinds. I studied and qualified in homoeopathy and acupuncture before attending the World Holistic Health Conference, where I saw one of Thornton's presentations. Harry Oldfield's methods and techniques appealed to the scientific part of me as they offered a rational explanation for the phenomenon I was personally experiencing.

'Electro-crystal therapy now forms the scientific basis of the major part of our energy medicine work at the Jesus Christ (JC) Diagnostic Centre in Worli, Bombay. Bombay is an area with 25 million inhabitants. Many have very limited financial resources. Energy medicine offers cheap, non-invasive diagnosis and treatment which can be administered in small centres with low overheads. I even heard Harry talking earlier about a clockwork version of the electro-crystal generator which could be wound up and used for hours at a time before simply needing to be rewound. The health implications of this simple technology could be enormous. This is especially true in a country like ours where there is a great deal of poverty and less general availability of electrical power than in most Western countries. Villagers tend to be suspicious of electricity.'

'Even so,' we suggested, 'surely the average Westerner would prefer to wind up a portable energy balancing therapy machine rather than plugging it into the mains or using expensive batteries. This would involve absolutely no cost in terms of powering the unit and would conserve finite resources that are currently being used in the generation of electricity and to make the materials for batteries.'

'Yes, I am sure that is so,' agreed the doctor. She continued:

'In India, we have what are called "barefoot doctors". These people are trained as paramedics under a government scheme which is intended to make some form of medical care available in every village. Barefoot doctors offer both allopathic and non-allopathic medicine. A qualified doctor visits the villages once or twice a week. But with very limited resources, there are generally no X-ray machines or other conventional diagnostic instruments because these are so expensive to provide and maintain. And there is always the cost of the staff to operate them. This is what would make Harry's ESM diagnostic system and electro-crystal therapy treatment such ideal weapons in the armoury of the bare-foot doctors in their war against disease and suffering in India.

'I am looking forward to the clockwork version of the electro-crystal generator.'

ASHOK SACHDEV

Electrical Engineer and Electro-Crystal Therapist

We also spoke to Ashok Sachdev, one of Dr Yamuna's colleagues from India.

'I'm an electrical engineer. I worked in industry, then I started on my own in the telecommunications field. I had been deeply involved in mysticism for many years before first coming across Harry's work a couple of years ago. I went to a demonstration of PIP at a friend's house. Given my background, the idea and the simplicity of the system "clicked" with me instantly. After enquiring further about Harry's work, I attended a foundation course about three months later.

'PIP is so interesting because "believing" in energy fields is different from "comprehending" the idea, which is different again from actually "seeing" the human energy field with your own eyes, albeit on a computer screen. Even people in India, who grow up with chakras, Ayurvedic ideas and so on, are very impressed when they can actually *see* what they know, by intuition and from thousands of years of practical experience, must be there. This aspect of PIP, that is, the making of the invisible visible to all of humanity, must not be underestimated. It is going to be big ... and soon.

'There has been a huge change in human thinking about energies throughout the world anyway during the last few years, but this new technology is so significant because of its real-time visual aspect. To know that you *are* an energy field, because you can see yourself as you really are on a screen, is so much more convincing than being asked to *believe* that you are an energy field because someone else tells you that they see you that way. And the hardware is so simple in concept and design. It can be set up on any computer, with any video camera, anywhere in the world.'

IT WORKS LIKE CLOCKWORK

Harry talked to Dr Yamuna about the timescale for the clockwork machines.

'Well, the schematics would take about half an hour for me to work out with the right engineer, but the little practicality of finding the resources to actually produce them in volume would, as usual, be the one and only stumbling block.

'Money for myself is a secondary consideration, although I do have a wife, a young son and all the normal expenses. Just like anybody else, I need to make enough money from my work to be able to live. Unfortunately, so far, this is all I've been able to do. There are so many projects I could be getting on with if there were some research and development funding available. But, unfortunately, when you come up with ideas to help humanity which are cheap to produce and buy and which don't cost lots in terms of keeping them working for people, you seem to find that industry isn't really interested because, by its very nature, industry wants to "produce things cheap, sell them expensive" and, if at all possible, make the consumer pay to keep the thing running.

'This is true of any modern business and I can't really blame them for wanting to make maximum profit. But there are some industries which should, in my view anyway, be run more for the benefit of people than for maximum profit. Call me old-fashioned, or even a do-gooder, but that's my opinion. The most obvious of these "people industries" is medicine. One doctor looked at the cost of my machines and dismissed any potential therapeutic value *purely* on the basis that it must be useless if it was so inexpensive. He wouldn't even look at it. Now that we're in the process of trying to reduce the overall cost even further by producing a clockwork version, heaven knows what the medical and pharmaceutical industries will make of us. We haven't got a hope of persuading these big business interests that helping people is more important than making large profits, so I suppose we'll just have to soldier on until some visionary, perhaps a Richard Branson or Isaac Tigrett type, gets to hear about our work and decides to back us.

'As you both know, the clockwork idea is certainly not new. Most people have heard about the clockwork radio which came on the market recently. The idea is that you give it 60 winds and it runs for 30 minutes. When it stops you wind it again. Simple, cheap, environmentally friendly energy. Wonderful. This is a concept which could make our human energy-field balancing machines a world-wide phenomenon in healthcare, especially preventative medicine.'

THE FLOURISHING POINSETTIA

Anne Catchpole is an electro-crystal therapist who can personally vouch for the positive effects of electro-crystal therapy on plants. This is part of a letter she wrote to Harry and Eileen:

'It is 28 December and I am inspired to write about my Christmas poinsettia. It is a real delight each day now with its beautiful bright red bracts, even more so because it is not this Christmas's plant, but last year's! I have achieved something wonderful with the help of electro-crystal therapy.

I had this large plant from a good farm shop last year. After it had faded I decided to put it into a spare room and not throw it out. I watered it occasionally and in the summer, forgot it! It looked dead, but I revived it, having decided to give it electro-crystal therapy D10 water treatment (the clinical electrode placed in the water jug for 10 minutes only).

At the beginning of December, I wanted to give it the best chance for Christmas so I repeated D10 water each week – just a liberal watering. To my excitement, by mid-December, pinkish bracts were appearing. These became darker red and larger each time I watered it – within 12 hours of every D10 watering the size and colour became much larger and brighter.

So for Christmas I had five large red heads (not as large as the new plants in the shops, but mine are more natural and are a joy to look at). I am so thrilled that I just had to write to tell you.

By the way, for the past 10 years I have never used an indoor plant fertilizer – just D10 water and TLC (tender loving care) for all of my healthy house plants.'

THE AUSTRALIAN CHIROPRACTOR

In the summer of 1997, Jane wrote to all the people she could think of who might be able to contribute something to this book. Jeremy Hirst, a chiropractor and electro-crystal therapist who practises in Victoria, Australia, was the first to write back. Here is part of his letter:

'As far as stories go, well, there are many I can think of! One instance where I have used electro-crystal therapy in conjunction with other therapies and good results have been achieved is the case of a middle-aged woman who had a slipped disc (L4 disc protrusion). She had been in severe pain and bedridden for two weeks, during which time she had been given ultrasound, infrared laser, soft tissue work and spinal adjustment to the L4–5 level, none of which had helped to ease the pain. So as a last resort I lent her my electro-crystal machine over one weekend, telling her to use it on anti-pain/anti-inflammatory settings over the injured site for the whole time, except when the batteries in the machine were being recharged.

I called back on the Monday evening after work and to my

delight, and hers of course, all the pain had disappeared. She was stiff still and unsure when moving, but the pain had all gone and in my opinion only an injection of cortisone/anaesthetic would have had a similar effect and this would have been painful, risky and almost certainly only temporary.

This is an excellent example of how electro-crystal therapy helped achieve control of pain in a very serious muscular-skeletal condition as well as being an excellent anti-inflammatory with absolutely no side-effects.

As far as other stories go, the two I like most are the Ministry of Defence story when he boots them out of his clinic and the tale of the Arab with harem problems and his bodyguards. Ask Harry to elaborate.'

We did.

THE SHEIKH'S HAREM PROBLEM

Harry was intrigued to hear that a man in his late sixties was coming to see him because prostate problems were causing marital difficulties with his wives. Harry learned that he was a sheikh who had such regular and arduous marital duties to perform that the regime would have tested the youngest and fittest of husbands. His prostate was swollen, causing pressure on the urethra and many visits to the toilet in the middle of the night.

'His Highness came to me as he had heard that the treatment could help him avoid an operation,' said Harry.

On the day of the appointment the sheikh arrived complete with an enormous entourage. The first to enter were four massive bodyguards. Two of them frisked Harry whilst the other two rushed up the stairs – presumably to ensure the absence of assassins in Harry's suburban semi! With the safety of their sheikh assured, the bodyguards allowed Harry to carry out the PIP scan.

'On the PIP the base energies were low, as expected,' he said, 'and we treated with stimulating frequencies. We only had three treatment sessions due to the sheikh's short period of time in the country.'

A little while after the third session, Harry was disturbed one evening by a loud banging on the front door. He opened it to find the four shadowy figures of the sheikh's bodyguards standing outside. His first reaction was panic. Had something gone wrong? Were they going to take it out on him? Was he being kidnapped? Then the translator appeared behind the four silent figures and behind him a huge Rolls Royce Silver Ghost gently pulled up. The sheikh got out, smiling broadly, and Harry began to relax a little. The translator broke the ice.

'His Highness was out for a drive this evening and decided to pay you a surprise visit to express his gratitude. You see, he has been to famous clinics in America and Switzerland and spent many thousands of dollars and francs with no change in his condition at all. In your humble clinic he has spent a few English pounds and there has been an immediate improvement.'

'Are you sure there has been an improvement so soon?' enquired Harry in his best deferential voice.

'Oh yes,' enthused the interpreter, 'in fact his Highness entertained three of his youngest wives last night and they report a complete and total recovery.'

'Marvellous,' said Harry, trying not to smile.

The sheikh's prostate problem continued to improve rapidly and Harry and Eileen were soon invited to a posh London hotel for dinner. When they arrived, Eileen discovered she was the only woman there and she was immediately escorted to her own end of the long table. The translator began talking to Harry as soon as the food was served.

'Now, sir, we would like to put a proposal to you. We are prepared to offer you your own hospital in our country. In addition you will have a little palace, not a big palace like his Highness has, but a palace nevertheless. In addition, we noted that you admired the Silver Ghost Rolls Royce. You will have a car just like that one. In fact you can have a different car for every day of the week if you wish.'

Harry considered pinching himself under the table to make sure he wasn't dreaming.

The translator continued. 'You will also have servants. We know you like your animals. Your cats will have their own servants.'

And so it went on.

The offer was extremely tempting but in the end Harry decided that such a move would be disruptive to Anthony's schooling. Furthermore, the Middle East was a volatile place at that time and could involve dangers which he did not feel able to subject his family to. He was, however, very pleased that his therapy had created such an impression.

Having received Harry's polite letter declining his offer, the sheikh still wanted to express his gratitude. A courier arrived with a box. Inside was a gleaming gold watch.

THE VET

Richard Allport is a veterinary surgeon who runs the Natural Medicine Veterinary Centre in Potters Bar, Hertfordshire. He is an innovative practitioner who uses both orthodox veterinary science and complementary therapies such as acupuncture and electro-crystal therapy to heal his animal patients. Richard has written two books on natural therapies for animals in which electro-crystal therapy is mentioned: *Heal your Cat the Natural Way* and *Heal your Dog the Natural Way* (Mitchell Beazley, 1997). He also writes regularly for various magazines.

Richard tells many 'doggie' stories and tales of other pets who have responded well to electro-crystal therapy.

'I went to a lecture given by Harry Oldfield at "Alternatives" in Piccadilly. I remember thinking, This guy's amazing! His energy and enthusiasm were astounding. Here was a man who, like me, had come from a conventional scientific background yet was moving into new areas. This ran parallel to what was happening in my own life. I had been through conventional training at veterinary college but now, as my work expanded into new fields like homoeopathy and acupuncture, I felt that I had to move beyond the boundaries of accepted science.

'During his lecture Harry was very clear in his explanation of how electro-crystal therapy worked. It made a lot of sense. He demonstrated the therapy on a few volunteers, who all reported good results. I liked the fact that the therapy had a scientific basis and that objective measurements could be made before and after treatment.

'I went to an introductory day where I learned more and decided that this just felt right – a non-invasive therapy which doesn't involve the use of needles and which obviously works. Not only would I be able to treat my animal patients, but my family too!

'I use the therapy in my day-to-day practice but not as much as I would like. Not many animal owners have heard of it, so they tend to choose the better known treatments like homoeopathy. I would love to see this effective therapy promoted more. So I have tended to use electro-crystal therapy in conjunction with other therapies and have found it extremely beneficial.

'For example, take the case of Jake. He was a rather overweight German Shepherd dog whom I was already treating with acupuncture for a painful spinal condition called spondylitis. I suggested to Jake's owner that we add electro-crystal therapy to his treatment.

'Jake had suffered symptoms of spondylitis for about a year. When first seen by me, six months previously, he had been almost completely without use of his hind legs because of the severity of the spinal condition. Weekly acupuncture therapy had helped enormously in that he was more mobile. However, improvement seemed to have stopped – a plateau had been reached. I hoped that electro-crystal therapy might cause more improvement to occur. Another factor was that Jake was not a friendly dog. He had

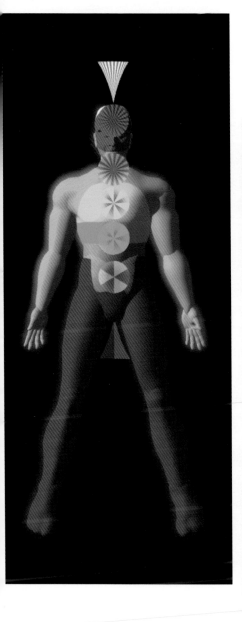

Here we can see the chakra system represented by Chakraman. The seven colours associated with each chakra are specific to electro-crystal therapy.

Above: This 'before' PIP scan was taken about two weeks after the whiplash injury was sustained. Note the red congestion around the neck and the right side of the head. This corresponded with the area of physical pain and tension. Also note the turbulence in the energy field around the upper body and head, especially the line of red energy which is 'leaking' away from the field from just below the patient's right ear.

Below: The patient was treated once a week with electro-crystal therapy and one month later, this 'after' PIP scan was taken. The difference appears to be marked. There is much less red congestion and less turbulence in the whole energy field. This corresponded to an improvement in symptoms reported by the patient.

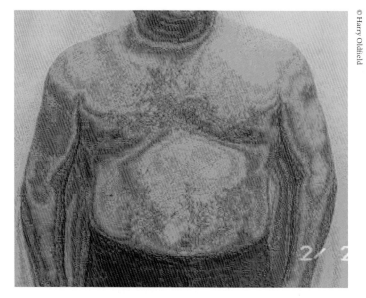

Above: The red and magenta lines and patterns in this person's PIP scan show areas of congestion and turbulence in the energy field, i.e. where the energy is not flowing as it would in a well-balanced field. These patterns are generally present in areas of known disease/trauma. Here we can see red/magenta imbalances over the throat (thyroid disease), pancreas (diabetes), liver (high alcohol consumption) and right arm (muscle strain).

Below: This person was then given hands-on healing. As the two healers entered his field, a few seconds after the first image had been captured, the two white lights above his shoulders appeared to descend, most of the torso went green and the solar plexus chakra seemed to burst open with yellow light. The base chakra is possibly being energized, as evidenced by the boxer shorts turning red.

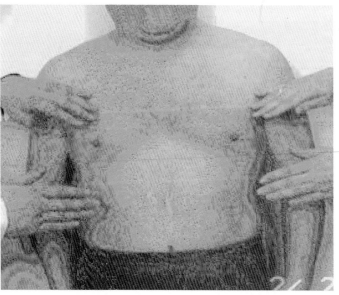

Above: Harry has long been investigating the relationship between mathematics and life. This has led him to become interested in fractal equations. These numbers, when fed into a computer, generate images which often appear to be like patterns found in Nature.

Below: Harry's investigations have sometimes led him down unusual avenues. This image was captured with PIP in connection with his research into the energies present in mortuaries. A number of observers have suggested that the image appears to be of a bearded priest-like figure who is wearing a 'hat' and has a staff in his right hand. Harry has named him Angelos. A vortex of energy appears to be emanating from the region of his mouth. Harry speculates that there may be 'collectors of souls' who are present in places such as hospitals and mortuaries, perhaps to guide the recently departed to 'another place'. Could Angelos be such a being?

been, before retirement, a guard dog for a security firm and didn't like his visits to the veterinary clinic. It was becoming increasingly difficult to insert the acupuncture needles without being punctured myself! I was hoping that, if effective, electro-crystal therapy might take over and – as it is a non-invasive treatment – that Jake might accept it with less aggression.

'Attempts to ESM scan Jake had to be abandoned swiftly. Even with his very helpful owner to hand, Jake was more than a match for both of us! I decided to treat Jake simply on symptoms present and use frequencies for "low back pain". At this session it was possible to insert some acupuncture needles and give about 10 minutes of electro-crystal therapy on the site of the spondylitis on the back.

'At the next session Jake's owner reported that the dog was less stiff than he had been for some weeks. So I repeated the combination of electro-crystal therapy and acupuncture for the next six treatments. I found I had to modify the electro-crystal treatment, using slightly higher frequencies, for progress to be sustained.

'By session 10 Jake had improved so much that I thought it was worthwhile trying the electro-crystal therapy alone. This I did for the next couple of sessions. But by session 12 Jake's owner reported a deterioration in the condition, I could detect more pain and stiffness along the lower back again, and Jake had more problems in walking. Once again I treated with acupuncture combined with electro-crystal therapy and a marked relief of symptoms was noted.

'It is interesting to note that apparently neither acupuncture nor electro-crystal therapy on their own gave as much improvement in Jake's condition as using the two together. It does seem that certain individuals respond better to the use of more than one therapy at a time. Perhaps there is some sort of synergism between the two.

'Although I started Jake on the standard setting of quite a low frequency for low back pain I was prepared to use a higher frequency as I often find that animals respond better to higher frequencies than those used for humans. On the lower settings Jake felt some relief, but he responded extremely well to slightly higher frequencies. The reason for this might be that smaller animals like dogs and cats have higher metabolic rates than humans and this affects the treatment needed. Perhaps the use of other high frequencies for longer would have done the job with electro-crystal therapy alone. I would like to do further research on this.'

BUCK'S STORY

Buck is the man whose story Jane remembers vividly from her training days at the School of Electro-Crystal Therapy. Here he tells it in his own words:

'In 1989 I was diagnosed as having a large brain tumour and I had a major brain operation to remove it. My family were told that the doctors didn't know what kind of tumour it was and that I had six months to live.

'After the operation I couldn't see at all well. I wasn't sleeping and was having panic attacks. I heard about Harry Oldfield and how he'd helped other people and I thought I'd give it a try. The first time I went I was carried in by two friends. Harry put his equipment on me and I went into a deep sleep. After that very first treatment I felt that something had happened to me. I couldn't put my finger on it, I just felt better.

'After a few weeks of seeing Harry, I'd go home as usual and lie on the settee. Then, out of the blue, POP! POP! My right eye opened and then my left eye and I could see again! It wasn't like my eyelids opening, it was more like *inside* my eyes or head.

'The doctors were very surprised at how much my eyes

had improved. I used to tell them about Harry, but they did-n't seem interested.

'After about five months of seeing Harry, I had to go to another London hospital for a new kind of brain scan. I had to lie in this machine for about half an hour. To take my mind off it all I'd close my eyes and say my prayers. Then the doctors decided that they would do some radiotherapy. I had a special mask made, which I've still got, and went every morning for 30 days. The doctors said that this treatment would burn away the tumour.

'At this stage I was still unable to move my left arm and leg. I then had another brain operation. Afterwards I was able to move my left side! My surgeon and a professor came round to see me. The professor looked at my charts and at me. He turned to my surgeon and said, "We're looking at a miracle."

'They let me out of hospital a week after that. Within that week I was delivering menus to the other wards in the hospital!

'It's now nearly eight years since the whole thing started. I lead a full life. I drive a car. My last scan showed that the tumour had completely gone – much to the doctors' surprise.

'I would like to say that all the time that Harry treated me he did not accept a penny from me. I received so much help, not only from Harry, but from the many other people I met at his clinic.

'Thank you, Harry, for taking care of me and being such a loyal friend. Thank you for the book you gave me and the words you wrote in it. They mean so much to me.'

Buck smiled fondly as he showed us the book Harry had given him. The words inside read: 'To my friend Buck. Happy Birthday to a very brave man whom I'm proud to call my friend in Christ. Harry Oldfield, 13/9/91.'

DR MAYSOON ABDULLA

Dr Maysoon Abdulla, originally from Iraq, is a member of the Royal College of Physicians. She is a forensic medical examiner, works as a clinical assistant in the rheumatology department at a large teaching hospital and is also an experienced electro-crystal therapist. Jane went to talk to her at her London home.

When Jane was shown into the living-room, she noticed a pigeon sitting in a washing-up bowl which had been made into a cosy bed. Food and water had been placed inside it. A plastic mesh laundry basket turned-upside down over the bowl prevented escape but still allowed a view. Dr Abdulla explained:

> 'He's broken his leg and can't move the toes on that side either. I assume the leg is paralysed. Not only that, but he hasn't got any tail feathers. Probably a cat got him. He can't possibly fly yet so I'm looking after him until he's well enough to fend for himself. I'm using electro-crystal therapy on him and he's responding well.'

Recently Dr Abdulla told us that she let the pigeon go after three weeks of treatment. His fracture had healed and he had recovered most of the movement of his toes. His tail feathers had grown. Two weeks after his release, she saw him near her home. He looked well and was bouncing with life.

Dr Abdulla explained how she had been introduced to electro-crystal therapy:

> 'In 1991 I began hearing about complementary medicine and was curious to find out more. A friend told me to contact the Institute of Complementary Medicine in London and they sent me a list of therapies. The first one I picked out was electro-crystal therapy. I went along to one of Harry Oldfield's introduction days and then on to the course. I liked the fact that the therapy is scientific and there's nothing mystical in it. I was surprised at Harry's depth of

knowledge. I remember thinking he must be very clever to know so much without having been to medical college.

'Electro-crystal therapy is just amazing. I am so astonished at the response. It is one we just wouldn't get with orthodox care! The therapy seems to work on a different level in its effects on the living organism.

'I treated a young man with hepatitis B. Treatment with electro-crystal therapy was commenced on the day that his jaundice appeared. [Patients with hepatitis B are ill for a few weeks prior to the appearance of jaundice.] Response to electro-crystal therapy was dramatic. He was able to leave his bed in a few days. The improvement in his jaundice and the return of his liver enzymes to normal were much quicker than we typically see. In fact they took about two thirds of the usual time. What is also interesting is that he completely bypassed the convalescence period, which generally lasts from three to six months, during which many patients feel extremely tired. He was playing football within two months! We just don't expect that response in orthodox medicine.

'I also treated a neighbour who had ME. He'd had it about a year. Normally he was fit and active, but with his illness he was exhausted and depressed. When I scanned him, his energy was extremely depleted. He came regularly, twice a week, and after about a month his energy levels started to improve. Within three months he was back to normal and back to work.

'I must also tell you about the man who pulled a muscle in the back of his leg whilst playing tennis. He'd been to his GP and a physiotherapist, who both told him that it would take six weeks for his muscle to heal. He came to me in desperation a day after the injury as he wanted to go skiing the week after! He arrived on crutches, hardly able to put weight on his injured leg. After three days of treatment his leg was back to normal and after five days he went skiing with no problems.

'I don't think that these responses can be put down to the placebo effect. I will give you an example – a lady with lupus. [Lupus is an auto-immune disease where the body attacks itself. Symptoms include hair loss and lesions on the face, reminiscent of a wolf's markings, hence the name.] After electro-crystal therapy not only did her blood results improve, but her face healed without scarring. [In orthodox medicine scarring is inevitable in discoid lupus.] The patch of alopecia on her head also healed without scarring and the hair regrew. She had renal involvement with haematuria [blood in urine from kidney] and had been on powerful medicines, with no response. On treatment with electro-crystal therapy her kidney disease improved and her haematuria dropped to minimal, coupled with that her blood tests for lupus dropped (DNA Ab% Binding from 76% to 29% and DNA Binding Ab IU from 104iu to 48iu). In this case there were two important points; one was healing without visible scarring, which is not possible with current orthodox medical treatment, and the other was the healing of the internal organs.

'I treated another lady with an inflammatory auto-immune disease. She had severe muscle weakness and had been treated with steroids and other strong medication in order to control her disease. She did respond to orthodox treatment but was kept on a low dose of steroids. She was very interested in complementary medicine. What was interesting was that, although her disease was well controlled with medication and was almost in remission, when I measured her energy field it was still disturbed. After lengthy treatment with electro-crystal therapy she had an amazing recovery and stopped taking the steroids. Her muscle strength went back to normal and her energy levels climbed, also her clarity of mind and intuition improved.

'Here again we find that electro-crystal therapy works not only on the physical body but also on other levels, perhaps even in another dimension not recognized in orthodox medicine.'

'WOMEN'S PROBLEMS'

Carrie Haines looks very good for her age. She is 50 years old and proud to admit it. This was not the case when she first came to see Harry for treatment. Fatigue had aged her. Jane remembers her on her first visit – a frail figure, her eyes heavily ringed by black shadows. She looks a very different woman today. Carrie is so delighted with her progress that she willingly shared her story:

'I'd heard about electro-crystal therapy from a friend at a tai chi class. He suggested that I should give it a try as it had helped him with a very serious illness. I really was in a bad state having recently been diagnosed with uterine fibroids. The person who did the ultrasound scan said that the fibroids were just "this side" of being operable. (What did this mean?)

'I subsequently had an appointment with my gynaecologist, who gave me some tablets to take if the bleeding got out of control. I was completely perplexed by this as I felt the bleeding was already out of control! I was experiencing extremely heavy periods for 14 days every month and the pain in my pelvic region was often so intense that I could only manage to walk for about 10 minutes at a time. This condition had gone on for months. At Christmas I couldn't even do my Christmas shopping because of the pain and bleeding. I was sleeping 10 to 12 hours a night. During the day I had just enough energy to keep up with my freelance work. My husband Michael had to do all the household chores as well as take care of me.

'I knew things couldn't go on like this so I decided to try electro-crystal therapy. I had high hopes but was still sceptical. I remember, the week before I first went to see Harry, joking to a friend that I was going to see a "witch doctor".

'Michael had to drive me to my first appointment with Harry. I hadn't driven for quite some time as I felt too weak and my level of concentration was poor. By the following week I felt mentally up to driving, which was a major step forward for me. I went every week for a couple of months. By the fourth week I was a different person, certainly a healthier one, and friends commented on my changing appearance. The permanent dark rings around my eyes had gone. My skin was brighter and I stopped looking like a ghost. My periods changed dramatically. They gradually went back to a six-day cycle and in the end they were so light, lighter than ever before, that I remember thinking, This is weird, what's happening?

'I now have my life back again and I can participate fully in all the things I enjoy. My sleep pattern is normal. I can walk with no pain and no longer have depression caused by endless PMT and excessive bleeding.

'I have electro-crystal therapy about every three weeks now as an effective insurance policy! I recently had an internal examination and my doctor said that the fibroids, whilst still "with me", are reduced in size – from a grapefruit to an orange! I will continue to come to Harry for regular check-ups, a bit like having an MOT!'

THE NORTH EAST LONDON CANCER HELP CENTRE

The North East London Cancer Help Centre, known as 'Sue's House', has helped hundreds of people suffering with cancer. Frank Longcroft is Trustee Administrator of the centre. He heard about Harry Oldfield and his work through an article in a local newspaper.

'I contacted Harry about the newspaper article and eventually joined the course and completed my training in April 1990. Since then I have offered electro-crystal therapy in my centre and have used it with some 350 cancer patients alongside relaxation, visualization and other therapies. I have found that electro-crystal therapy has proved to reduce stress and toxins significantly. It has also been useful in treating pain and it has the ability to stimulate or tranquillize the energy fields and therefore bring about a wonderful balance and harmony to the whole body, which gives the patient a wonderful feeling of well-being. As a complementary therapy this can be used for so many conditions. It is so rewarding to see the amount of success that can be obtained from it.'

ARTHRITIS AND BACK PROBLEMS

The pain of arthritis is suffered by millions. Modern medicine offers some relief in the form of painkillers or anti-inflammatory drugs, but many people are so affected by or worried about side-effects from these drugs that they choose to live with their pain.

Mrs Ramsden has arthritis in her neck and degeneration of the intervertebral discs. She decided to come to Harry's clinic for electro-crystal therapy:

'The doctors couldn't help me. They told me I had osteoarthritis, gave me some painkillers and said there was nothing more they could do. We came here to Harry's with our eyes open and thought, Either the therapy will help or it won't. We didn't come with blind faith. I just thought I'd give it a go as I had nothing to lose.'

Mr Ramsden asked if he could say something at this point.

'The possibility that the whole treatment thing could be a con did cross my mind. But I soon had my mind put at rest on that score.

'The thing that impressed me the most when we first came to Harry's clinic was a cat that had cystitis. A treatment tube was put on a chair and the cat jumped up on it deliberately! Well, you can tell a human about the therapy and there's the possibility that they can be conned, but you can't con a cat. It went and deliberately sat on the tube. And it got better.'

Mrs Ramsden continued:

'I was having an extra bad time with arthritis in my neck, which had been getting progressively worse over 30 years. Every time I turned my neck more than about 45 degrees there was a cracking noise. I'd get pain if I stayed in one position for more than half an hour, during the day for instance if I was reading or typing. I'd had acupuncture years back which alleviated the pain for a while but I lost touch with the acupuncturist.

'My back was a problem as well. The discs were degenerating. Every morning my back would get "stuck" for a while after I got out of bed. From time to time something would set my back off. Something as simple as getting a saucepan out of the cupboard would do it and I'd have to go to bed.

'I came to Harry in the September and he said that things would be much improved by Christmas, which they were. After the first treatment I felt extremely sleepy going home in the car and I didn't notice much difference in my condition. In fact I thought that things were a little worse the day after each treatment, but once that was over then things would improve considerably until I saw Harry the following week. By the fourth treatment I was a lot better.

'Now, 11 months on, things have definitely improved. No more getting "stuck" when I go into the bathroom in the morning! My neck is a lot better. I rarely get any pain and if I do it's minimal. The cracking has virtually stopped. I can type or read for an hour now with no problems. I'd recommend this treatment to anyone with arthritis. There aren't any harmful side-effects and I'm certainly feeling better.'

GUY PILBEAM, THE BUDGIE AND THE FARMER'S WIFE!

Guy Pilbeam is an electro-crystal therapist who lives in Shakespeare country. He kindly wrote to us about some of his experiences when treating animals and people:

'The first case was that of a budgie belonging to farmer friends. The farmer's wife phoned to say that their budgie was lying on the bottom of the cage with its exposed eye blinking slowly. All her five young children were in tears, as the vet (who had called to tend a cow) had said it would die within the hour. I said I would try to revive it and rushed over with the electro-crystal therapy equipment. I administered a high-frequency energy boost to the budgie and within five minutes it was pecking its owner's hand. I left some water which I had energized using the same high frequency for it to drink and made two more visits for treatment of 20 minutes. That was two years ago and the bird flourishes to this day.

The second case involves the farmer's wife, whose legs were run over by her Land Rover. [Yes, that's exactly what Guy wrote! We didn't ask.] After 10 days in hospital and no end of physio, she was left holding one leg in the air like a stork. She could not physically plant it on the ground. The doctors were at a loss to know what treatment to give. I lent her a small electro-crystal therapy machine and gave her various settings, some to calm the pain and others to energize the leg. Within a week she was walking almost normally and now goes to karate lessons weekly.'

THE BULGARIAN DOCTOR

Dr Anna Philippou qualified as a doctor after completing seven years of medical training at the Medical Institute 'Tchervenkov' in Sofia, Bulgaria. She later studied acupuncture and homoeopathy. It was at the Hahnemann College of Homoeopathy that she met Harry Oldfield, a fellow mature student, and learnt about electro-crystal therapy. Dr Philippou provided us with three instances of her experiences with Harry and his work:

THE INGROWING TOE-NAIL

In the case of an ingrowing toe-nail, I can report that the infection had just started and the inflamed big toe had been aching for about six to seven days. A very short five-minute session of electro-crystal therapy cured the inflammation like magic.

PIP DIAGNOSIS BY HARRY OLDFIELD

I took a 53-year-old lady along for a PIP scan. She had a big hard growth in the lower part of the abdomen, the size of a baby's head. We suspected that she had a large fibroid in her womb.

Harry carried out a PIP scan and his interpretation of the picture was that the growth was consistent with *fluid*. Soon after, the lady went to her local hospital where an ultrasound scan was performed. This revealed that she had a large ovarian cyst which consisted of fluid and calcifications. It was definitely not a solid fibrous tumour (fibroid) as we had first thought. Both I and the patient applauded Harry's PIP scan invention.

SUCCESS IN TREATING JOINT COMPLAINTS WITH ELECTRO-CRYSTAL THERAPY

Mrs B. had severe inflammation of the knees and feet, accompanied by painful swollen joints. She noticed a reduction of the inflammation and pain after the first electro-crystal therapy treatment. Later the pains almost disappeared, but they reappeared after Mrs B. took some self-prescribed homoeopathic tissue salts. She was advised to stick with electro-crystal therapy, since it had hitherto been suitable and beneficial for her condition.

Conclusion: If there is improvement whilst using electro-crystal therapy, it is better not to introduce other therapies for as long as the condition continues to improve. Do not mix therapies, unless you are already having treatment with another form of therapy and the introduction of electro-crystal therapy assists with progress. We have found that electro-crystal therapy does not produce any side-effects and that it can be used alongside any other complementary or conventional treatment. If there is aggravation of the patient's symptoms, we are certain that the aggravation is not caused by electro-crystal therapy. But this therapy may not always be sufficient in itself to treat a particular case and symptoms will be seen to continue.

PIP AND COLON CANCER DIAGNOSIS

Mary came to Harry's clinic for a PIP scan soon after she had been diagnosed with cancer of the colon.

'I live locally to Harry and thought I'd come along for one of his PIP scans. I wasn't at all sure that I understood what I was letting myself in for, although I liked the idea that it all sounded very scientific and not at all "airy-fairy".

'Between diagnosis of my tumour and the operation there was a month's gap and it was during this time that I had the PIP done. Harry showed me the distinctive energy pattern in the area of the tumour. It was really clear to see. He said that it was localized, which was very reassuring. He also pointed out that the energy to my immune system was low, that I had a build up of stress on my head and that there was evidence of toxins in my liver. Amazingly, he saw that

I have problems with my right hip, which I hadn't told him about! He was certainly right about the stress too.

'I was really impressed with this guy who sat there with such confidence in his system – so impressed that I decided to try some of Harry's treatment machines too. So I managed to fit in two treatments before the operation. After the first treatment I felt nothing, but after the second, as I went out the front door, I had to stop as I had the most immense tingling in the top of my chest, over my thymus gland. I couldn't believe it, so I went back in to speak to Harry. Harry said that this was normal, just the energy to the immune system balancing itself out.

'Again I was impressed. Something had happened and I hadn't expected it. Harry deliberately doesn't tell people what to expect. The tingling went right down to my elbows and lasted about two hours.

'I had another PIP scan after my operation and what a relief to see that the energy of the cancer had gone. The liver looked a lot clearer and the energy to my immune system was 75 per cent improved. Whenever I had my down moments in the weeks after that, whenever I wondered whether the cancer had really gone, I would get out my PIP scan pictures and immediately felt encouraged and reassured. They were positive reinforcement for me, something I could see.

'Hospital scanners are so expensive and can only be used for people who are already ill. My surgeon and I chatted about how wonderful it would be if there were a national screening campaign and then problems could be picked up in the early stages. I thought of Harry and his relatively inexpensive PIP scanning equipment. At the risk of looking a fool, I'm going to show my surgeon the PIP scan pictures next time I go.'

THE NURSING CARE ASSISTANT

Terry Hunt is a nursing care assistant and a recently qualified electro-crystal therapist. He was introduced to electro-crystal therapy when he took his brother, who has multiple sclerosis, to see Harry. Terry was so taken with the therapy after seeing the improvement in his brother's health that he decided to enrol on the course. He says:

'I really enjoyed the course weekends. They've opened up a whole new world to me. The clinical practice days, which I had to do as part of the course, were also great. It was very helpful seeing so many people being treated with electro-crystal therapy. I feel it has really reinforced the therapy in my mind.

'I have managed to see quite a few people at home and we've had some tremendous results. The range of cases has been enormous. There was a man who had a bad ulcer on his foot which wouldn't heal. The surgeons were planning to amputate, as they were worried about gangrene setting in. But after a few treatments, the ulcer had healed sufficiently for the surgeons to have changed their minds about surgery.

'I treated a friend who'd had a frozen shoulder for a good six months and had been taking anti-inflammatory drugs for the pain. I put a flexible tube electrode at the back of his shoulder and over the shoulder blade and started treatment. He felt a surge of warmth which travelled right through his shoulder. He's had no problems since, no pain and more movement in his arm. Before the treatment he said he had to keep moving the arm to help alleviate the pain. Well, he doesn't have to do that anymore. It's been nearly a year now and he's had no further problems.

'My dear old mum has been absolutely delighted with her electro-crystal therapy. She went to the doctor about pain in her knees which started following a fall in the street. He told her that she was getting old and that he thought arthritis was setting in. We thought we'd give the therapy a go. I used the standard settings for painful knees and also treated the energy to the base of the spine. The pain went immediately. She'd had some marks on her legs for years – they looked a bit like bruises. Well, they went too. She also had some fluid retention in her ankles and I used the standard settings for that. Now that has gone as well, she has "top-up" treatments from time to time.'

SPORTS INJURY

Bill Bennett is a keen footballer who has had more than his fair share of injury sustained on the pitch. When he broke his arm very painfully during a match, the ambulance that came to take him to hospital was in need of resuscitation itself. It broke down! Bill talks about his experience with electro-crystal therapy:

'I broke my arm in a footballing accident. It required the insertion of two metal plates and 13 screws. After the operation, I used electro-crystal therapy to calm the inflammation and to ease the pain as well as to get rid of some rather ugly keloid scars. Occasionally, the end of the metal plate would rub internally, causing a painful swelling. Using the therapy would not only take away the pain but also disperse the swelling completely.

'Three-and-a-half years later, I have had the metalwork removed and am now using electro-crystal therapy for the effective relief of post-operative pain and for calming the whole wound area, which is a little swollen. I have found that when using electro-crystal therapy, particularly on a pain-relieving setting, I get the most wonderful tingling sensation going up my arm and down to my fingertips. As a result the whole area feels more comfortable and far less delicate, not just while the treatment is switched on, but also afterwards.'

THE SINGER

Loretta Heywood, a singer, decided to try electro-crystal therapy:

'I had heard about Harry through a friend. I went along for treatment for knee problems and general tension in the body. It's now two months since I started treatment and my knees are greatly improved. They are by no means perfect, but there has been a dramatic change – they are not as stiff as they were and it feels as though something is loosening up inside them. My neck, though, still needs treatment.

'Sometimes I would go along for treatment feeling anxious about something. I would have a tightness in my chest and the sensation of a tight wire in my head. After treatment I would go out quite calm. I feel that the therapy has helped to balance my emotions as well as balance my physical body. I feel as though my chakras have been washed out. I am generally happier and can cope better with stress. Something inside has shifted in a positive way.

'Without you even really knowing what is happening, electro-crystal therapy shifts your energy. This treatment definitely holds one of the keys to open the door to the answers inside ourselves.'

COMBINED THERAPIES

Pauline Galvin is an experienced reflexologist, kinesiologist and electro-crystal therapist. She uses PIP to augment her diagnostic techniques.

'I combine electro-crystal therapy with reflexology and kinesiology as well as using it on its own. It is an invaluable tool which allows me to calm, balance and stimulate areas of the body which I have found need particular attention whilst treating with reflexology and kinesiology. I always perform a sound (ESM) scan to confirm my findings. One of my most valuable aids is the PIP scan which I carry out prior to treatment with any of my therapies.

'Areas of disturbed energy on the PIP scan, which often show a "plus" reading on the sound scan, are frequently found to have "over-energy" in the acupuncture meridians. This can be addressed kinesiologically using the sedating meridian contacts. Having corrected the "over-energy", other areas of the body which showed up as disturbed on the PIP scan frequently balance themselves out. This can be confirmed by taking a sound scan – the "plus" reading is found to be considerably reduced.

'A "minus" reading over an organ on the sound scan can be due to "under-energy" caused by "over-energy" in the preceding element on the Chinese Shen cycle, both of which will show up as disturbed areas on the PIP scan.

' "Over-energy" or "under-energy" in an organ will show up as a muscular pattern on PIP. For example, if the liver has "over-energy", the pectoralis major sternal muscle on the upper chest will often be seen as an imbalanced pink-red colour, as well as there being imbalance over the liver itself. This liver energy imbalance can be corrected with electro-crystal therapy or reflexology or kinesiology.

'Each set of muscles in the body is driven by one of the 14 acupuncture meridians. Frequently energy is blocked in a muscle because it is starved of lymph and blood circulation, thus blocking the energy flow to both the muscle and its organ. If the latissimus dorsi muscle on the back is in spasm due to back problems, the spleen and the pancreas will show a disturbance on the PIP scan. When the muscle has been worked on and the lymph, blood circulation and meridian energy are flowing through it once more, the disturbances in the organs will disappear. However, if there is a problem with either the spleen or the pancreas, this will frequently manifest as discomfort in the muscle in the back, causing back problems, since one muscle has a knock-on effect on the other muscles.

'As a reflexologist and a kinesiologist the PIP scan is invaluable to me. For example, if someone is complaining of pain in the muscles of the lumbar spine and the muscles either side of the back of the neck, I check kidney meridian flow. If a problem is found with bladder/kidney meridian flow you will frequently see on the PIP scan that the prostate at the front (in a man) and the kidneys at the back showing up clearly as congested areas of energy.

'I scanned a lady with tunnel vision and was amazed to see a circular energy configuration, the size of a 50 pence piece, at the back of her head directly behind the optic nerve, which was badly disturbed in this instance.

'A lady with fluid retention and kidney problems was discovered to have a bad diet in that she ate too much fatty food and this caused "over-energy" in the gall bladder meridian – which showed up on the PIP scan as the anterior deltoid muscle, running from the clavicle to the upper arm, looking very red and disturbed. This gave me a clue as to the problem – the "over-energy" in the gall bladder was blocking the energy flow from the bladder and kidneys once again on the Chinese Shen cycle. Once her diet was modified – and she was found to be sensitive to milk, cheese and butter, which she ate a lot of, believing it would prevent osteoporosis – the fluid retention problem ceased.'

MARMALADE THE CAT

In 1996, Marmalade the cat had a severe car accident. Her back hind quarters were crushed, she lost the end of her tail, and bowel and bladder control were non-existent.

'When she came to me she was in a terrible state,' said Harry, 'but as you can see, two years later she is jumping in and out of her basket.'

Marmalade was purring away.

'What is the significance of cats purring at alpha rhythms?' we asked.

Harry replied:

'Well, evidence has shown that people who are neurotic, or who have high blood pressure, heart conditions and so on, respond well to alpha rhythms. I think that cats and other animals may interact with humans via something called biofeedback. The cat purrs at about 10 cycles per second and this helps entrain the human being into the same state. Another term for this entrainment or inducement of a similar state is "sympathetic resonance".'

THE DORSET THERAPIST

Lin Brady is an electro-crystal therapist. She and her husband, John, run a complementary therapy clinic in West Moors, Dorset. Lin offers both electro-crystal therapy and PIP to her clients. Like many therapists, she is increasingly finding that the opto-crystal therapy device is extremely effective in certain cases. She told us about some of her experiences.

'Mrs Hill came to see me. She had been suffering with earache, on and off, for eight years. The medical profession couldn't find anything wrong with her ear. When she arrived for her first appointment, she had earache. This had started the day before. Normally the pain lasted for about four days. I applied the aquamarine opto-crystal therapy accessory to her throat area, which had shown an imbalance on ESM scanning.

'The blue light pulsed through the aquamarine crystals for about 20 minutes, after which time Mrs Hill reported that, amazingly, the earache had gone. She said she could hardly believe it. The pain did come back after about three weeks, but was not as severe as it normally was and did not last as long as usual. Mrs Hill is continuing with treatment.

'Another lady, Miss Johnson, has been coming for treatment for thyrotoxicosis [over-active thyroid] for the last couple of months, during which time she has reported feeling progressively better. Two weeks ago she arrived for her regular appointment in tears. She was having a bad day and feeling very low, upset and fearful. I used the aquamarine light on her throat and after about 25 minutes she said, "I can only think of one word to describe today's treatment: *powerful.*"

'She then told me that she felt very much more assertive and stronger in herself and asked if she could have the blue-light treatment next time.'

LUNG TRANSPLANT OP CANCELLED

Sheila Sheridan is the patient mentioned earlier who believes she was saved from a lung transplant operation because of her electro-crystal therapy treatment.

'I was first introduced to Harry Oldfield and his electro-crystal therapy by a very close friend who was already attending his clinic. I suffer from a very severe lung condition and was told by my consultant that a lung transplant was imminent.

'I started treatment with Harry and within weeks I felt things were changing for the better. I had a lot more energy and began to feel my old self again. I continued seeing Harry for about three years as my hospital tests were improving all the time and a transplant was not mentioned again.

'Then my husband had to change his job and I found it difficult to get to Harry's clinic. I had not been for about six months when I started to feel unwell and was admitted to hospital. My consultant started to mention the dreaded transplant again. After discharge from hospital, I soon got in touch with Harry and he saw me straightaway. I started the electro-crystal treatment again and, once more, within weeks things started to improve. When I went back to the hospital five weeks later for tests the doctors could not believe the improvement!

'For the past two years I have continued to improve and have my own electro-crystal machine at home. I use it every day for about 30 minutes. I still have all my own "parts" and it's all thanks to Harry and his wonderful therapy.'

NO SEX PLEASE, WE'RE DECEASED!

As the perspectives in this chapter show, Harry certainly meets a wide variety of people. He once met a medium who sat next to him at a dinner function. This lady was a spinster of the archetypal maiden aunt variety.

'Wehhhlllll,' she began telling Harry out of the blue, 'you know, young man, that there is no infidelity or jealousy on the other side, don't you?'

'Oh, really,' said Harry, barely able to contain his amusement. 'And why is that then?'

'Because there's no sex!'

Harry thought for a moment and couldn't resist a smile.

'In that case, madam – I'm not going!'

THE 'H-FILES'

'We go about our daily lives understanding almost nothing of the world.'

CARL SAGAN

S OME of the stories surrounding Harry and his work are so far outside the normal human experience as to warrant being called the 'H-Files'. We have selected some of the more interesting encounters to share with you.

MEN IN BLACK

During 1981, an article in *Medical News Weekly* mentioned that 'The idea of playing the radio waves back, at the individual's resonant frequency, and disintegrating them smacks of science fiction.' The magazine was making a serious attempt to analyse the merits of Harry's work for medical diagnosis. However, the contents of the article sparked a visit to Harry's home by two men in long coats who, whilst offering no formal identification, had 'the aura of people who are used to being listened to', according to Harry. This is what happened.

Just after Harry had finished his clinic for the day two men arrived on the doorstep. It was raining. Actually, it was pouring. Thunder rumbled in the distance as Harry ambled up the hallway to answer the bell. Two lean shadowy figures filled the doorway behind the frosted glass.

'Good evening, Mr Oldfield. May we come in?' said the smaller of the two unexpected visitors as Harry opened the door a few inches.

'Um, well, what is it that you want?' was Harry's understandable enquiry.

'We represent a government department, sir. We'd like to talk to you about your work.'

Harry got the feeling that these men were not going to go away without the talk.

'OK, but it's all very mysterious,' he said defensively.

They went through to his living-room and the two men made themselves comfortable without waiting to be invited. Nevertheless, in every other way, they were polite and respectful, almost overly so, thought Harry.

'Now, Mr Oldfield, we will get straight to the point. We've been taking an interest in you and your work for some time. As a citizen of the United Kingdom, can we assume your commitment to the national security of your country? In short, sir, would you say that your country could depend on you as a patriot?'

'Undoubtedly,' said Harry, wondering where all this was leading.

'Good. Now we note that your machines appear to have the capacity to heal and integrate the energy fields of sick people.'

'Yes, that's my life's work.'

'Well, if we told you that the Soviets are working on ways of disintegrating and harming the energy fields of the healthy, could we count on you to serve your country by designing similar instruments?'

It was made clear that sufficient resources would certainly not be a problem.

'Ohh, that's a difficult one,' began Harry, thinking quickly. There was no way he wanted to design something that was meant to harm people. Any people. His whole life had been devoted to doing just the opposite. He had always wanted to harmonize and heal, not disintegrate and destroy.

'I'm afraid my belief system might get in the way,' he continued, trying desperately to find the right way to say no as politely as possible. 'You see I'm a Christian and ...'

The mood of the men changed. The bigger one frowned and looked at the floor. The smaller one spoke.

'That's quite a disappointment, Mr Oldfield. We were very much counting on your patriotism. You see, the Americans already have this and ...'

'Well, I'm afraid there will be no movement in my position,' interrupted Harry forcefully and asked the pair to leave immediately, rather to their surprise.

Officially, of course, this meeting never happened.

Harry was worried for quite some time afterwards that he may have gone on some sort of 'blacklist', but he heard nothing further and presumes that the relevant department got someone else to do the job.

Whilst we were talking on this subject, Harry mentioned a related aspect of the Gulf War:

'When some of the disabled Iraqi tanks and other armoured vehicles were opened, the men inside were found with blood coming out of every orifice. Their organs were disrupted but the vehicles were fully intact, even the electronics. So, it begs the question as to whether these weapons have already been developed and used.

'We can only speculate as to whether this is what happened, but President Reagan seemed prepared to use the Star Wars weapons against the Soviet Union, didn't he? Most people allow for the possibility that ray guns and energy field disintegrators could be the weapons of the future but these highly efficient methods of killing may be undergoing limited field testing in conflicts at the moment. I for one don't like that idea. These sort of weapons could make nuclear warfare seem like child's play.'

CROP CIRCLES

Harry was asked by some people connected with the Ministry of Agriculture to look at aerial video footage of a number of crop circles. He was also given stalks, soil, plant and grain samples from the circles, together with 'control' specimens from the same area but outside the circles.

'Some of the crop circles had distinctive energy patterns when I ran them through the PIP system. I was told later that the circles we identified with PIP as having the distinctive energy fields were in fact the ones which the researchers were least able to explain.

'Also, the grains from these "genuine" circles had become magnetized. It is certain that some strong force did it, but what that was is, of course, open to speculation.'

MIND OVER SPACE

Dr Periclis Charos lives in Athens, where he practises orthodox medicine and osteopathy. In common with many of the new generation of forward-looking medical doctors around the world, he also offers energy medicine in the forms of PIP, electro-crystal therapy, reflexology, radionics and Bach flower remedies. As can be seen from the impressive list of therapies and techniques available at his clinic, Dr Charos has a wide range of interests. Bending space with his mind is another of them.

This is, of course, an area of his research which might be considered very forward looking indeed by some of his more conservative colleagues. But now that he has PIP, a scientific instrument, to work with, he feels that some headway may be made in persuading others that this is a plausible area of research.

We were at the School of Electro-Crystal Therapy the morning when the 'mind over space' pictures taken with PIP arrived from Greece. Harry showed them to us.

'I believe, and so does Dr Charos, that Einstein was right when he said that space and time were inseparable. You can't have one without the other. And we also believe that space can be bent by thought, which is a form of energy. As you can see from the notes that Dr Charos has made, the energy configurations – the shapes – under the light bulb change when he directs his thoughts at them, whilst all other conditions remain constant. The only variable is his thoughts, so we might logically conclude that it is the thoughts which are influencing the energy changes.

'We still have a long way to go, but this early research is very encouraging. I've also conducted experiments in which PIP shows that as we stress metal, the space around it also bends.'

PHYSICIAN'S THOUGHT FORM ON THE PIP SCANNER?

Dr Richard Gerber, the American doctor who first suggested to Harry that he might develop what subsequently became the PIP system, talked to us in December 1997.

'Harry PIP scanned me the last time I came over to England. It must have been 1993. I had come over to lecture at the Royal Society of Medicine. I had actually flown in that morning. I stood against a white screen and Harry took the PIP scan.

' "That's interesting," he said. "There's a large zone of red over your lower back. Have you got a back problem?"

'Two years previously, I'd had a problem with my lower lumbar spine and had suffered with sciatica, but as it had significantly improved, I had forgotten about it. As Harry drew my attention to it, I was aware that there was a dull ache in my lower back, no doubt due to the long plane journey.

'I asked Harry if I could try an experiment. Harry readily agreed and continued scanning me. Without telling Harry what I was doing, I visualized a stream of white light going down through the top of my head and through my spine. As I was visualizing this I could hear Harry saying, "That's interesting. A column of white light is forming behind your spine."

'I was intrigued. The PIP scan was showing exactly what I was visualizing. How fascinating that a thought form could be captured on the scanner.'

We asked Dr Gerber for his views on the future relationship between orthodox and complementary medicine.

'There is a greater movement, within orthodox medicine, towards acceptance of complementary medicine techniques. I am on the International Advisory Board of the Dove Health Alliance, which is the sister organization of the Dove Health Trust, in England. It's an international consortium of researchers, scientists and complementary healthcare workers. At present we're waiting for funding to come through for research into complementary health techniques which we're planning on conducting in Russia, England and the States and, hopefully, Australia.'

KUNDALINI

Back in 1986, Harry took a very interesting Kirlian photograph which he believed to be the first firm evidence for the existence of the legendary kundalini life force. It was published in the *Journal of Alternative Medicine* and showed the base of a woman's spine before and after treatment. The woman, in her early 50s, was suffering muscle spasms from a trapped nerve.

Harry thought that the 'before' picture showed the 'blocked' or 'interrupted' energy flow and the 'after' showed the life force, or kundalini energy, flowing freely in its classic coiled serpent mode. He explained:

> 'The base chakra is said to be a storehouse for a natural and very powerful energy known as kundalini, which has the potential to activate and align all of the major chakras. Normally it is slumbering in the base area, and people such as yogis attempt to release and raise it from the base to the crown in a well established sequence to reach spiritual enlightenment.
>
> 'However, sometimes the kundalini can release itself or be released in cases of accident to the base of the spine or drug taking or ill-advised meditational practices. In these instances it is like releasing a tornado in a confined space and the consequences for the individual whose body it happens in can be catastrophic.
>
> 'You must remember here that we are talking about the energy of life, the animating life force itself. It is tremendously powerful.'

Much later, in 1995, Harry was able to capture a 'before' and 'after' PIP picture of uncontrolled kundalini energy:

> 'A young woman came to see me in a distressed state. She found that she was affecting electrical equipment, for example, TV sets would switch on or off when she walked in a room or other equipment would fail.
>
> 'She was also very disturbed by what she called "telepathic communication from across the world", which involved hearing voices and so on. This had started a few months previously.'

Harry proceeded to carry out a PIP scan in the normal way except that he saved each picture separately in case the young woman affected the apparatus. Despite this, when he went to view the saved pictures, they had been wiped from the system.

Harry started doing the pictures again and then, suddenly, the computer crashed. Only one image had been saved. Harry comments:

'A highly energetic release of uncontrolled kundalini could be seen between the woman's legs. There were violent storms of energy swirling around her feet, invisible to the naked eye of course.

'This single saved picture also showed a thick bolt of energy coming from her right foot towards the computer just before it crashed. Amazingly, this bolt of energy obliterated the view of her leg, it was that powerful.

'Fortunately, this story has a happy ending. By some strange coincidence we had a healer at the clinic that day who was able to administer hands-on healing in conjunction with electro-crystal therapy.

'The combination seemed to work because the next week the young woman returned and we were able to carry out a PIP scan with no problem. She reported that all the disturbances had ceased and she was very much more relaxed.'

THE GENERAL PRACTITIONER

Dr Aubrey Hill served in the Fleet Air Arm during the war. He studied for his medical degree at St Bartholomew's Hospital and qualified in 1956, then spent several years in general practice. He is also a qualified homoeopath. He met Harry Oldfield quite a few years ago:

'Memories of Harry come crowding in. The first time I met him I remember his enthusiasm as he described his therapy. I also remember the lunches and the Chinese meals! I am still in touch with one or two people from those early days.

'One weekend Harry came up to Norfolk for a weekend

seminar I had arranged and fascinated a large audience, some of whom I think are now practitioners. He kindly brought up a device for treating ears which afterwards I used quite frequently. Although I used electro-crystal therapy quite extensively and with some good results, I slowly cut my workload down and now specialize in homoeopathy.

'However successful a form of treatment may be, it needs a philosophy behind it. I am delighted that Harry has carried his research forward to the point where he is talking about life-forms in his beloved crystals. I have studied Teilhard de Chardin, who was another deeply religious Catholic scientist. I am reminded of de Chardin's theory – which is perhaps more a philosophy or a way of life – that saw evolution continuing from the material to the spiritual in a seamless movement. Teilhard thought that life must proceed from pre-life. Contrary to the prevailing beliefs, he did not think that complex living things evolved from more simple living things. He believed that living things evolved from material entities which others believed to be non-living and containing nothing that could lead to life.

'I therefore congratulate Harry for his courage in stepping into places where few people have gone before.'

AN UNUSUAL VIEW FROM DOWN UNDER

Dr Brooke J. Keller and Dr Wayne A. Goss run a clinical practice in Melbourne. They sent us their story in November 1997:

'We had heard so much about Harry Oldfield and his wonderful work and had read his book *The Dark Side of The Brain*. Here was a man we had to meet!

After a long trip from Australia, via the US, we turned up unexpectedly on Harry's doorstep. He had a day off – what a day to choose! But luckily, his lovely wife Eileen was home and, as she probably remembers, two-and-a-half hours of chatting time just flew by.

The next day we met Harry and he obligingly suggested taking a PIP scan of Brooke to demonstrate his work. The analysis was spot on, a thyroid problem was observed and a recent back injury was evident with an energetic disturbance showing up in the lower back region. We spent quality time, if only briefly, with Harry, but we had seen enough to convince us to return six months later, in February 1995, to be the first Australians to study and qualify to use the PIP scan 'down under'. We also studied electro-crystal therapy.

When training, our first patient was a Mrs Smith with her arthritic dog Rex. How lovely it was to see everyone at Harry's clinic extending a warm welcome to our four-legged friends as well as to us humans. We were touched and impressed by how Harry would waive treatment fees for children and animals and would never turn away anyone truly needing help who was unable to pay.

During the evenings, we set up our PIP system at the house where we were staying, as we needed to practise. We had been concerned about a friend of ours, Peter, whose whole being had been very disturbed. Many times we had experienced him going into "turns" of being choked and trying to fight off what was choking him just to gain the next breath, or we would be out enjoying a meal together and he would start chatting to something unseen. He was incapable of sitting still, his legs were constantly jiggling, he often displayed several different personality types during the course of the day and he was very unable to make and stick with a decision.

We set PIP up and began scanning Peter. Then we saw something truly amazing. There was a python-like creature swarming around him. It appeared to attach itself to the neck region (fourth to fifth chakra level) and rotate itself around the waist and genital areas of his body. We had thought he might have an "entity" or "entities" attached to him and now we had tangible proof of this, both for us and our patient.

The first night that we scanned Peter and observed the entity phenomenon we were unable to save the images on the computer. For some reason the hard drive memory storage crashed. We found out from Harry the next day that this can happen, as entities seem to have an unknown level of intelligence.

So next evening we set up the equipment again after rebuilding the computer's complete operating system. Peter had had a very trying day and was very agitated. (Perhaps his entity did not like being discovered?) He was shivering and vomiting by evening. This was possibly being caused by the entity knowing of the plan to scan him again later that evening. As we scanned his body we could see it again! This time we were able to capture the images by saving each one directly to floppy disk, leaving little opportunity for the entity to launch another attack on our evidence.

As we hadn't received our electro-crystal therapy equipment at this stage, we were unable to include this modality in the healing session that Peter had requested. But over the next few hours we performed, to all intents and purposes, an exorcism on him. His death-like screams of horror rang out through the neighbourhood whilst we utilized aromatherapeutic bathing and essential oil etheric cleansing, Reiki and Chiron healing modalities.

Peter was absolutely exhausted by the end of his healing. We were certainly pumped up with adrenaline and totally worn out by it all. Peter stayed over that night and awoke a happy man – a golden radiance flooded his face and his eyes sparkled with joy! As we were leaving that day for Copenhagen, we asked Peter to attend Harry's clinic to follow on with further etheric energy field maintenance with electro-crystal therapy. To this day, some three years later, Peter has not suffered any recurrences of this problem. Thanks to Harry's technology another person has regained peace of mind and quality of life.

During our training time with Harry we had an Australian patient, H.G., on whom we had used essential oils as part of his healing session. After the healing session and studying all day, Brooke was feeling a little tired so decided to take a little therapy time for herself. She chose to have a bath and put some essential oils in. She chose, without consulting Wayne – who is a trained aromatherapist, – neroli and rose. (Perhaps the reason Brooke didn't consult Wayne was that these were the two most expensive oils in their travel kit!) A few drops proved to be too much, since she had been using essential oils with H.G. just a short time before. As she got out of the bath she realized that she had put herself out of balance. She had the most uncomfortable feeling, as though her bladder was full all the time, and the pressure was agonizing! Brooke kept the problem to herself as she felt that one patient in the house (H.G.) was enough.

When we arrived at Harry's the next day, Brooke's problem was soon discovered. The PIP scan revealed that her choice of essential oils had over-stimulated her base chakra, causing a "kundalini flare". She was also losing a great deal of energy from the base energy centre. Harry immediately asked Jane to apply electro-crystal therapy to her base chakra region. Within a few minutes she was out of pain and feeling fine. Thank you again, Harry!

We use many forms of vibrational healing modalities at our newly established clinic in Melbourne. Our healing strategies involving bio-energetic medicine include electro-crystal therapy, PIP scanning, cymatics, frequency resonance therapy and many other techniques.'

PLASTIC-EATING BUGS

One day, as he finished a training course that we were helping with, Harry threw in a little aside about his current thinking on a particular form of physical pollution which, he said, had potentially catastrophic ramifications for the planet if we did not take it more seriously ... and soon!

'This threat is from world-wide plastic poisoning,' he continued, 'but I think I've developed a plastic-eating bug which could literally change the world's approach to the disposal of plastics.'

With that mind-blowing throwaway, Harry smiled, touched his nose conspiratorily, winked, turned and went.

The plastic-eating bug with a taste for PVC and similar material was in the back of our minds for many months but it was not until we decided to do the book that the full story of this micro-miracle unfolded. Harry began the tale:

'I was invited to Iceland by some scientific colleagues with whom I had earlier established a good rapport to both teach and administer electro-crystal therapy. Whilst there I expressed a wish to visit the volcanic desert which I had been told so much about by my Icelandic friends.

'When we arrived at the site, which is still kept secret to avoid unwelcome visitors, I was amazed to see a huge expanse of black sand which stretched out before us between two mountain ranges. Walking on the sand, I noticed large amounts of what looked like dark green plastic material spread all over in small lumps on the ground. The pieces were mostly the size of a biscuit.

'My hosts told me that the "plastic" stones were in fact green opal. I found this difficult to believe, given the evidence of my sense of sight and touch, and wondered whether a large amount of plastic material could have been deposited here and melted at high temperatures under-ground then redeposited in the black desert by, perhaps, an erupting volcano or some other natural process.

' "Harolder," they assured me, "this is definitely green opal and you can take some home to have it analysed." '

Harry's eyes lit up as he told us that Harolder means 'mighty warrior'. He continued with his story:

'Icelanders are very spiritually and psychically aware people as a rule. There is of course the Norse mystic tradition of rune culture, Viking sagas and so on, but my feeling would also be that these high levels of psychic awareness may be something to do with their geographical proximity to the North Pole, which probably exerts a strong electromagnetic influence over them. Whatever the reasons for their sensitivity, the Icelanders were genuinely concerned that our age would be remembered for the harm it did to the planet.

' "Harolder," I was asked, "what do you think this geological age will be remembered as in 10,000 years' time?"

'I pondered a little and then speculated, "The Oil Age?" '

According to Harry, the Icelanders' view was that our time would be remembered as 'The Plastic Age' or, more likely, 'The Plastic Pollution Age'. Whilst 100 years is no time at all nature's terms, in just one short century we will have deposited such a huge amount of non-degradable plastic substances all over the globe that in 10,000 years that may be all we will be remembered for.

The problem with plastic is that nothing breaks it down naturally to any effective degree. When a plastic substance is deposited, it is, of course, subject to some natural mechanical action such as weight of rocks, weathering, sand-blasting by wind-driven particles, water erosion and so on, but none of these has any significant recycling effect.

Iceland is warm underfoot in places. It is a very new part of the Earth geologically and displays what the Icelanders called a very strong 'auto-immune response of the planet' to all the pollution it is having to cope with. So it actually appears that in Iceland the suffering living planet is producing green plastic-like opal, green being the colour of balance.

Harry came back and had the green plastic-like opal tested at the geological museum in London. Sworn to secrecy, he was not able to divulge the exact location of the source of the material. Nevertheless, the museum confirmed that it was indeed a true mineral, 'opalized'. Harry was gravely concerned.

After this worrying episode Harry immediately set about looking into the ways in which nature disposes of 'plastic-like' substances such as insect and crab shells. As usual he thought that the natural world might hold the vital clues.

He buried some of the insect and crab material in his garden and waited. Various micro-organisms began their work of decomposition. Harry scraped them off into a Petri dish. He experimented for quite a while, feeding the bugs at first wholly with natural 'plastic' substances, then gradually breeding successive generations which could make do with less and less of the natural 'plastic'. Simultaneously, he encouraged the 'hungry little monsters', by various ingenious means, to develop a taste for unnatural or man-made plastic. Eventually he had a plastic-eating bug that relished man-made plastics.

'And,' says Harry today, 'their waste produce was a black substance which I used as fertilizer in my garden!'

It does not take much imagination to conceive how important work such as this may be in future in the protection of our environment.

Harry says, 'Burying plastic is like putting away a nasty time-bomb for our great-great-grandchildren. You might agree that naturally recycling it is a different matter.'

THE DRAGON PROJECT

In 1978, Harry began taking part in the Dragon Project set up by Dr John Steele. This project was concerned with geomancy, with 'the Earth as Gaia'. This is the idea that the Earth and all on or in it form one interdependent living organism, much like a cell.

The name of the project was derived from the Chinese concept of *ch'i* or *qi* energy, which is thought to flow like a dragon in, on and around the Earth. This energy wells up at certain 'positive' points on the Earth's surface and ebbs away at other 'negative' points. An analogy could be 'taps' and 'drains' where energy emerges and disappears, thus ensuring the 'flow of life' is maintained.

Harry was involved in Operation Merlin 2 (OM2), which took place at the Rollright Stones, Oxfordshire, at the summer solstice, and aimed to introduce new researchers and techniques to the project to see how they fared.

He arrived some minutes before dawn, having been delayed by car trouble. Aided by Eileen, he set up his advanced Kirlian equipment in the circle, as well as a device for measuring molecular resonance.

Harry's Kirlian photo of a megalith *in situ* was later described by Paul Devereux, who wrote up the project, as a 'notable first'. 'Clearly,' Paul went on, 'Kirlian work is moving into a reclaimed sphere of significance.'

BLACK SHEP

The Dragon Project included quite a lot of work at the Rollrights. Part of it involved carrying out some scientific measurements at the winter solstice, in late December.

Harry rose very early on the morning he was due to drive to Oxfordshire, but the anticipated A40 traffic jam was non-existent at that time in the morning and he cruised to the site in no time at all. 'I arrived at about 3 a.m., and not surprisingly, I was the first!'

Harry decided that, rather than waste time, he would get his EMG monitors (normally used to measure muscles in medicine) and other equipment set up. The white frosted grass crunched and crinkled under his boots. It was dark, cold and misty as he knelt down and took off his gloves to attach some wires. His hands froze around the equipment.

Suddenly the scientist was aware of being watched. Realizing he was all alone in the middle of nowhere, heart pounding, he reeled around to check his hunch. The mouth of a huge beast was inches from his face. Whew, it's only a dog! Harry quickly remembered he likes dogs.

The big black hound stood completely still, staring straight into Harry's eyes.

'Hello, boy,' Harry greeted him, reaching out to pat his short hair. He immediately withdrew his hand in horror. The dog was ice-cold and solid to the touch.

'Oh, my word, you're frozen, boy,' he comforted. 'Go home. Go on, go on.'

The dog stood staring, motionless, ignoring Harry's commands. Harry felt compelled to say something else.

'Don't worry, boy, I'm not hurting the stones.'

A few moments after hearing this, the animal turned slowly and padded out of the circle. Harry assumed he was going home and carried on with his work.

A few more minutes passed and Harry realized he had left his screwdriver in the car. He started crunching back out of the circle the same way that he had come in. It was then that he noticed something odd. The dog had padded out of the circle in this same direction – but there were no pawprints. Harry was intrigued. His own footprints were clearly visible in the torchlight. He searched for a long time inside and outside the circle. Nothing. Then he realized something else: that dog had no breath. His own breath was plain to see in those conditions. This was all very odd. Very odd indeed.

Arriving back at the car, Harry made a decision. He did not want to admit it to himself, but he was spooked. I'll stay here and wait for the others, he thought. Can't do much more now anyway.

He got in the car. And locked all the doors!

Alone and shivering, Harry sat for a further three hours until the rest of the scientific team began arriving. Then he quietly spoke to one of the local members of the group about his experience. The other man smiled.

'That'll be Black Shep. They call him the Hound from Hell. There have been reports of sightings since Roman times. According to local legend, Black Shep is the guardian of the stones. The last unexplained death was in the 1930s. A man had been desecrating the stones. His throat was torn out. He was unrecognizable. The case was never solved.'

BORNEO PEARL DRAGON

Doreen Jenkinson, who knew Harry from the days when he gave demonstrations at the Spiritualist Association, many years ago, told us how she came to get involved in his work:

'I attended one of Harry's lectures. He wired up flowers to an EMG apparatus and a loudspeaker. The plants seemed to have reactions to people interacting with them. This demonstration of plant/human energy interaction showed me that everything exists in a sea of energy.'

Before Doreen could continue, Harry, who had been studying his PIP screen, called us all over.

'Look at this picture, Jane and Grant. Doreen has just come back from Kinabulu mountain in Borneo. Natives who live at the base of the mountain believe it to be sacred.

'This rock from the top of the mountain is made of granite. The mountain is reported to be growing at the rate of a quarter inch per year. As you can see, the control background PIP picture shows very little energy, but the picture with the stone shows a very energetic bubble around the top of the stone's surface. It looks like a large pearl.

'The natives believe the dead live at the top of the mountain. There appears to be a photonic being in this crystal and perhaps this is what the people are referring to when they report seeing spirits in the stones at the top of the mountain.'

Doreen wanted the pictures to show to her native guide in Borneo. Harry put them on disk for her.

'The natives still report many sightings of these crystal beings,' she told us. 'So my guide will be very interested in Harry's PIP picture.'

ANT EXPERIMENT

Harry had a friend who trained in electro-crystal therapy. This man had a problem in the area of his solar plexus. He went on a family picnic and, having eaten his fill on a lovely sunny afternoon, laid down with a crystal tube curled around in a doughnut shape on top of his abdomen.

Some time later he was awakened from his slumber by his wife shaking him. She pointed to the tube. He looked down to see hundreds of golden meadow ants arranged in concentric rings around the circled tube. They appeared to have aligned themselves to the electromagnetic field created by the electro-crystal equipment.

SPACE-AGE SCIENCE

We have had various conversations with Harry about space-age science and medicine. In one we learned that he has been working on an artificial skin which could be sprayed onto burn victims. This would quickly solidify and keep in body fluids but allow the natural skin to breathe and repair itself. It would also act as a protection from infection.

We also learned that Harry had produced artificial blood based on silicon and saline products and chlorophyll. However, it looked like milk and Harry is still working on it.

Another of Harry's projects concerns his 'enzyme theory' for the treatment of cancer and abnormal growths. This would involve using enzymes from carnivorous plants. The carnivorous pitcher-plant, for example, grows in moist jungle areas and attracts insects rich in enzymes. The plant's fluid digests the insects' tough tissues and nitrogenous products are absorbed for the plant's growth. The relevant fluid from the plant could be used for destruction of solid state tumours. Ideally, only enough enzyme would be injected to produce a reaction.

'This would get rid of the tumour mass in readiness for a much less serious operation,' said Harry, 'as the fluid would dissolve the malignant tissue. Perhaps this could be a natural alternative to chemotherapy in both Earth and space medicine?'

Perhaps these techniques would be especially useful in long space journeys during which there would probably be no possibility of using human or animal donors as happens on Earth.

Harry has met a number of space-age scientists over the years and has exchanged some fruitful ideas, including 'some interesting thoughts about low frequency energy and cold fusion, which in theory offers the potential of producing huge amounts of energy in a kettle. What's interesting is that you get more energy coming out than you put in. The advantages in space over existing energy-generation techniques could be enormous. Safety is obviously an important factor on a spaceship.'

CLOAKED SPACESHIPS

Whilst we were talking with Harry about the possibilities of future travel throughout the universe, he suddenly rose from his seat, saying, 'I must show you something.' After furtively rummaging in a ground-level cupboard for a few moments he emerged, almost triumphantly, with a little mud-brown folder.

'Andrew Patterson, my physicist friend, and I had an interesting conversation about cloaked spaceships. I know it sounds a bit *Star Trek* and "Klingon War Bird", but have a look through that and let me know what you think.'

'What is it, the secret of invisible UFOs?' we asked, half joking, but really hoping it was.

'Well ... yes, I suppose it is really,' Harry replied without a hint of humour.

We couldn't wait to get home and look at the contents of the folder. We made a cup of tea and sat down. 'This should have "Top Secret" on the front,' we smiled to ourselves conspiratorially and proceeded to remove Harry's handwritten papers. To our dismay, much of the stuff was written in 'gobbledygook', a language consisting largely of pictures, patterns, signs and hiero-glyphics, which we could not make head nor tail of.

Getting back to cloaked spaceships, the readable part of the papers explained how the crew of a spaceship could use the prop-erties of light and the way it is seen by humans to 'cloak' their craft at will and so make it invisible to the human observer whenever required. They would do this by projecting the back-ground onto the front and sides of the ship. It made us wonder, given that Harry 'had the technology' from his garden shed research, whether governments might have done the same thing already? Would this explain the UFO phenomenon? This is at least as feasible as extra-terrestrial life-forms visiting us from other planets, given the vast distances involved.

Another thought we later discussed with Harry was that alien life-forms could be visiting us from other dimensions rather than from other planets in the known universe.

THERAPISTS IN CANADA

Professor and Vasana Spogliarich live in Canada. Their interest in energy rebalancing began in Italy, where the professor taught gen-eral and inorganic chemistry at the University of Trieste. Vasana Spogliarich was suffering from an undiagnosed virus that con-fined her to a wheelchair. When she couldn't get relief through traditional medicine, the couple sought help from Harry Oldfield. Later they trained in electro-crystal therapy and PIP and now run their own clinic. They replied to our request for more informa-tion about their work and research:

DARKNESS TO LIGHT

One of our most extraordinary cases was that of a young man who was blinded in a motorcycle accident. His right eye had lost fluid so the eyelid was only slightly open and after two operations his retina was still deteriorating and he was in danger of losing it. It was also thought that the left optic nerve had been severed. The most remarkable feature was that both eyes had been 'frozen' as if in absolute darkness, i.e. each eye was all pupil except that a pencil-thin line of iris was visible. His energy was low and he had various pains throughout the body.

Within the first two sessions it became obvious that the iris on the right eye was growing larger, beginning from top and bottom and then from the two sides. After several months the right iris had grown so much that it was almost normal. The retina was now red and healthy looking and the eyelid remained much more open as the fluid in the eye was building. All this was confirmed by regular check-ups, to the astonishment of his doctors. His eyesight also began to return and he was beginning to see car lights from 130 feet away and, therefore, confidence in walking and his safety were greatly improved. Also the pains were gone and his energy was up.

At the six-month mark the iris on his left eye slowly began to grow. The original PIP imaging and ESM scans showed lots of red energy and inflammation respectively, while the subsequent PIP was much greener and inflammation was down or gone in some cases. Unfortunately, we left the country before total eyesight was restored.

ENERGY LOSS

Two very interesting circumstances to do with 'energy loss' which PIP has shown up occurred while we were filming in Italy. In the first instance, we PIP scanned the head and throat of a young boy. The whole screen around the head suddenly flashed red – as fast as it had appeared it also disappeared, only to recur approximately 20 seconds later. Struck by the highly unusual behaviour of this flashing red energy we only commented on it. The next day the mother phoned to say her son had come down with chickenpox.

The second instance was when my (the professor's) PIP picture was taken. We saw a similar red energy which flashed across the screen, continually disappearing and reappearing. This occurred immediately after an afternoon on which I was totally drained of energy by someone who was extremely negative, bad-tempered and complaining. Knowing this not to be my usual pattern, we could only deduce that what we were seeing was, in fact, the effect of having the life force drained out of me. Several days later, after having recovered from that, we found that my image had returned to normal.

One anomaly which recurs fairly often on PIP is flashing movement and even blackness in the base of brain area. It may also be accompanied by an energy block. Many times a client will neglect to tell us of past or present depression; however, when we inquire, having seen these patterns, they will confirm it. In some cases it might be due to sleep disturbances or more rarely SAD (seasonal affective disorder), or possibly electromagnetic disturbance. The point is that PIP reveals the problem.

With people who have a history of very severe types of problem such as continual migraines with vomiting or old-age tremors (where the person's limbs shake with oscillations up to 8–10 inches wide), we see on the PIP an energy pattern which vibrates at an incredible speed, almost impossible to follow with the naked eye. Many times a quivering pale greenish mass is present in the area surrounding the disturbance. It has been noticed that even if our ESM indicates to calm the site down, the results are better if we balance it until subsequent PIPs show that this erratic pulsation has ceased.

PTOLEMAIC TERRASCOPE

To say the magazine *Ptolemaic Terrascope* falls into the category of 'unusual publication' would be an understatement. In the Winter 1990 issue (Vol.2, no.2) David Tibet is talking about his group Current '93, with whom Harry recorded his crystal music.

The band are described as an 'enigmatic outfit, whose albums fetch vast sums as soon as they're released, who are cult figures in industrialized countries like Germany and Japan, and yet who remain staunchly so deep underground as far as the UK music press is concerned that they might as well be buried'. David himself says:

'I never had any thought of becoming involved in music. I came to London to study Classical Tibetan and Buddhist philosophy. Eventually that's what I did, but that's another story.

'I bumped into Genisis P. Orridge, of Throbbing Gristle, one day in Portobello Market. I started working with him in the formative stages of Psychic TV and, more importantly, met John Balance, who went on to form Coil with Peter Christopherson, Fritz Haaman (then of 23 Skidoo) and Steven Stapleton of Nurse With Wound, a group I idolized along with Whitehouse.'

David went on to explain how he met 'HOH', a man from Iceland who helped him make his first album. This was Hilmar Orn Hilmarson, one of the people who took part in Harry's crystal-dwelling photonic being studies *(see Chapter 5)*. More albums followed, also trips to Iceland and Japan. The first in the 'Current '93 Presents' series was a collection of Tibetan Tantric chants sung by the lama under whom David had been studying, the Venerable Chimed Rig Rinpoche. Next came *Crystal Sound*, 'manipulations of crystals made to sing by the introduction of electromagnetic pulses into them by Harry Oldfield, an author and medical researcher and practitioner'.

We couldn't help thinking that David Tibet must be an interesting bloke. Harry told us he had found him and his friends charming and, true to their word, when they said they would get studio time for him to show them how crystals could sing, they did. As already mentioned, the resulting CD sold out all 10,000 copies in a very short time when it was first released. Harry has the master and today will make an audio tape from it for anyone who asks nicely – and provides a tape!

THE BUDDHIST LAMA

One day Harry was expecting a very revered and respected Buddhist lama for a PIP scan. The lama was attended by his personal assistant who helped him in as he was having a little difficulty walking.

Harry soon learned why. It was an incredible story. The monk had fallen down a mountain ravine, a sheer drop of 300 feet.

'As I was falling,' said the lama, 'I kept in mind what my spiritual teacher had taught me: whatever happens in life, it is important to enjoy the experience. I remember smiling to myself as I kept this at the front of my mind on the way down.'

'We found his eminence at the bottom of the ravine, unconscious, but with a serene smile on his face,' added the attendant. Harry continues:

'The injuries certainly were not consistent with a normal fall from that height. Most people would be fatally wounded.

'Then a very interesting thing happened with the PIP scan. The lama was positioning himself in front of the white screen in my office and I had the camera on him. The helper and I suddenly noticed, on the computer screen, a huge and vibrant aura and the most marvellous dancing lights all around the holy man. The light configurations seemed to be an array of symbols.

'Then the lama saw that the camera was on and running and that we were showing a keen interest in his "lights". With an enigmatic smile, he waved his hand and with that the phenomena ceased immediately and his energy field shrank to resemble that of a normal person.

'As you can imagine, I questioned what had caused what we had just clearly witnessed.

'With another smile, the holy man simply said, "This may be a case of 'non-sense', Mr Oldfield. You must see a great deal of such 'non-sense' in your work." '

THE FUTURE

'An important scientific innovation rarely makes its way by
gradually winning over and converting its opponents: it rarely
happens that Saul becomes Paul. What does happen is that its
opponents gradually die out and that the growing generation is
familiarized with the idea from the beginning.'

MAX PLANK

T HIS book tells the story of one man's search for healing
methods to help us survive the twenty-first century.
Harry's aims are simple. He would like to heal all the
plants, the animals, the people and the planet – and all in one
lifetime!

For the future, Harry would like to develop his ideas on the
diagnosis and treatment of disease and to promote well-being
according to God's plan wherever he can.

'I would especially like to see my PIP and ESM systems
developed for diagnosis in both conventional and complementary clinics around the world. And preventative medicine is probably the best form. Since we are measuring
the energy field, we could highlight potential problems at
the earliest feasible stage. Imbalances often appear in the
energy field before they manifest as signs and symptoms in
the physical.

'I would like to see clinics in the future offering both
physical and energy treatments of all kinds. These clinics

would have the right atmosphere with music and colour schemes conducive to healing and so on.

'In terms of conventional medical applications, I would like to see my energy field diagnosis and treatment methods undergo full clinical trials at some point in the future.'

Harry has been told that to test the effectiveness of his treatment machines clinically would cost millions of pounds, so it may be some time before this comes about.

On this point, Harry himself says:

'Of course, if a treatment method works, it works. And if people have a good experience they tell others. Given these factors, people will increasingly vote with their feet as more are introduced to our work. In a sense, this is a field test in its own right.

'And it would be lovely to see the portable electro-crystal therapy unit in every home. It would be like a sort of energy first-aid kit to give people the choice between a biochemical pill or an energy rebalance.'

Not only this, but Harry thinks he may also be able to make a contribution to the age of space exploration, 'which will probably be upon us sooner than we think', and he would like to address the problem of pollution, both in the physical and invisible realms.

'In terms of more down-to-earth science there are things like the smoke mask and ways of improving aviation and industry in general which do not harm the environment.

'Then there are the telescopic, microscopic, astronomical and other as yet unconceived applications to which PIP theory and technology may be put in the future. This is an open book as far as I'm concerned.

'Then there are the more unusual aspects of my work such as the crystal-dwelling photonic beings and the other energetic entities we have been able to image with PIP.

I would dearly love to visit the crystal mines of the world to see if we can obtain video footage of the crystal beings in their natural habitat.

'Another area of unusual research would be the continuation of ethical projects in which we have been trying to ascertain the nature of the energies which surround the body after physical death.

'I am also hoping to work with a psychology department in one of the universities in Europe on psychological and parapsychological projects.

'I can see huge possibilities for dissemination of our work through the World Wide Web. We could have all sorts of people contributing their ideas as to the implementation of instruments like PIP, for example. Who knows what applications will emerge if millions of people have access to energy-imaging devices such as this?'

Along these lines, when Mr Wee Boo Kuan of Valerie Physiotherapy Centre invited Harry to Singapore in August 1997, Harry's ideas were put onto Sintercom, an Internet site. During this visit, Harry explained that world comparisons may be possible with PIP. As he said,

'There is little difference in energy patterns between patients I saw here and patients from the UK. There were increased allergy disturbances in children and definitely stress-related patterns. However, there seems to be a relatively low incidence of people suffering from MS here in Singapore.'

The future of this comparative work is obviously huge.

Looking to the future of Harry's diagnostic and treatment techniques, there are now a number of variations on the general theme, including electro-crystal therapy, opto-crystal therapy and crystal sound therapy. A term has been devised which encompasses all of these variations: 'the EleCT Method', or 'EleCT' for short. The various training schemes which are offered by the School will fall into one generic category: 'the SEleCT Method'. From now on we will use these terms to describe either the clinical or training categories respectively.

As technology has developed, Harry has been able to refine his instrumentation and he looks forward to more progress in a number of areas.

One of these areas is the PIP system. As we know, a PIP prototype was ready in 1989. Since then it has been developed a great deal but Harry still feels that there is a lot to be done.

The early PIP was designed for the Archimedes computer. The programmer, John Catchpole, recommended this machine as the most suitable for the graphics programme at that time. Today, Harry has developed 'PIP's daughter' and she runs on any IBM-compatible machine with Windows 3.1 or Windows '95. Tomorrow, with the rapid advances in computer hardware, software and imaging technology, who knows what the granddaughter and great-granddaughter of PIP will be able to do?

Harry told us something of his hopes for the future of PIP:

'The main thing I want to see is the PIP system tested by doctors and scientists to see if they can use it to diagnose existing and even potential disease.

'I am quite prepared to participate in any properly controlled trials of any of my equipment. The one criticism that I do find unfair is when doctors say that I am mind-reading or using body language techniques to diagnose people with PIP.

'You must remember that when a doctor diagnoses, they ask an awful lot of questions and send the patient for confirmatory scans, tests and so on. I can often come to the same conclusions in a few minutes using the PIP scanner with far fewer questions.

'Before people make criticisms of this nature, perhaps it

would be fairer if they had actually spent a few years learning about energy medicine and familiarizing themselves with my equipment. Until they do that, how can they really comment? That's all I can really say on the subject.'

Many commentators foresee PIP clinics all over the world, perhaps linked via the Internet to central sites where experts like Harry could analyse PIP stills or videos sent in via the World Wide Web. He and other experts could then send out advice as to treatment settings with the electro-crystal therapy equipment which everyone could have in their homes. Harry says:

'This sort of thing is already happening in orthodox medicine. It is thought by some that regular trips to the GP could become a thing of the past because, by early next century, we will be able to get our ills diagnosed from home.'

Kenneth Boddy, lecturer in obstetrics and gynaecology at the University of Edinburgh and co-ordinator of the Edinburgh Healthcare Telematics Centre, agrees:

'It'll be like being in a video conference with your GP – or even a specialist, if that's what you need. If you had a pain in the chest, you'd simply put an electric monitor onto the painful area and, using your PC or television, link into your nearest telemedicine centre for advice from your GP. And if they couldn't help you, you'd just tune into a specialist who could.'

Harry expands:

'Telemedicine is already saving time and trouble for pregnant women attending St Mary's District General Hospital in Newport on the Isle of Wight. Rather than making visits to the mainland, if their ultrasound scan indicates they need a specialist opinion, they can be referred – by a BT video link – to a consultant obstetrician at the Queen Charlotte and Chelsea Hospital in London.'

Another potential use of PIP could be in monitoring the effects of ingested substances on the energy field. Harry explains:

'During my years of research with PIP, I have been able to monitor the effects that vitamin supplements, homoeopathic remedies and flower essences and such like have had on the subtle fields of the person taking them.

'I have also observed that conventional drug treatments can affect the energy body as a whole as well as altering the energy configurations seen around individual organs.

'There may be a future potential for PIP in assisting doctors when they are assessing optimum dosage of supplements and drugs. This could save on resources and in some cases save the patient a barrage of unwanted side-effects if the "best" dose was found to be a lot lower than that generally prescribed.'

It may be that energy medicine therapists would learn to 'read' PIP images as part of their basic training or as an addition to their repertoire of diagnostic tools.

As for the therapists of the future, they will probably be multi-disciplined. Today, many therapists are already qualified in other methods of treatment before they come across the EleCT Method, and the Institute of Complementary Medicine (ICM) has already been looking into the training of multi-disciplined therapists. The advantage of Harry's system is that it is ideally suited to work in conjunction with any other treatment and it gives a great deal of scientific rationale to the energist.

We have mentioned that methodical science is a key aspect of Harry's work and that many of his healing instruments can be tested and assessed according to established scientific principles.

Harry feels that evidence-based complementary treatments are now becoming part of routine medical care and this is a trend that looks set to continue.

He says: 'At University College Hospital in London, acupuncture is being used in antenatal care for common problems, such as backache and morning sickness. Many fundholding GPs are also buying in the services of alternative practitioners.'

Dr George Lewith, who runs the Centre for the Study of Complementary Medicine based in Southampton and London, believes the NHS is responding to rising demand for complementary medicine because it realizes that it is safe and effective in managing chronic illnesses.

Harry adds:

'It is vitally important that we have professional bodies for complementary therapies to oversee and maintain standards. We have set up a school to do just that for EleCT. In the future there will be an increasing need for such governing bodies as regulations from Europe and so on take more effect.

'I think the future will see more highly trained and properly registered practitioners in all complementary therapies, leading to higher standards. This will make it easier for more conventional doctors to trust these therapies.'

This could pave the way for a system of 'electro-medicine' with which we could reorganize, restructure and rebalance the human energy field, so putting in place the right conditions under which the physical body could begin to heal itself. The potential for such a system is believed by many to be enormous.

The ideal would perhaps be for orthodox medicine's universities to expand the training of new doctors to include a study of quantum physics and energy field medicine as well as the biology and chemistry they currently teach. This new science has been described as 'quantum biology'. Its incorporation into the mainstream would mean that the undoubted successes of orthodox medicine could be expanded upon in the light of this new knowledge.

Orthodox medicine *has* gradually begun to explore the uses of energy for treating illness. These include the use of radiation to treat cancer, electricity to alleviate pain and shrink tumours, electromagnetic fields to stimulate bone healing, and magnetic fields to alleviate the pain and inflammation of arthritis.

However, orthodox medicine will not become fully supportive of 'quantum biology' and 'electro-medicine' until a great deal more research has been done. In the meantime, the School of Electro-Crystal Therapy is offering one-year part-time training courses for domestic and overseas therapists (preferably with a prior qualification/working knowledge of anatomy and physiology), who can study for a practitioner's certificate and hence become qualified to provide a range of EleCT treatments.

In the two decades since its humble backroom beginnings, over 200 EleCT practitioners have already qualified and the therapy is now being practised, represented and reported on world-wide.

Unfortunately, in a 'Catch 22' situation, the people who are researching in this area are often considered to be unorthodox in the first place and thus find it difficult to get help with the financial strain imposed by the understandable requirement for stringent scientific testing. Nevertheless, a number of scientists around the world have made considerable progress in their research on very limited budgets, including, most notably, Harry Oldfield.

Harry would like to see combinations of vibrational and orthodox therapies offered under the same roof. 'For example,' he says, 'one use of electro-crystal therapy could be to try to balance the imbalances caused by the side-effects of some drugs.'

Harry appears to be a one-man army. Not only did he have to design, develop, build and test his diagnostic and treatment machines, but he also had to promote his work throughout the world to a wide and varied audience.

Part of this audience may learn of his work through the Internet, but Harry has always taken the message to the people at conferences, conventions, demonstrations and on his courses:

'In 1989 we attended the Second British Congress of Complementary & Alternative Practitioners. This annual conference and exhibition of natural therapies was held in London. Its aim was to look at "the future of training and education towards the evolution of an effective and appropriate system for the twenty-first century".'

The exhibition was organized by the *Journal of Alternative and Complementary Medicine*. Harry was on the journal's 30-strong advisory panel and he would like to be involved in this and many other ways in the future development of natural medicine. Harry also would like to have a magazine format to illustrate his diagnostic and treatment methods. As his team of helpers grows this is looking like a real possibility. He is also planning many more conferences and demonstrations of his work around the world and thinks that this, and research, will be the main thrust of his personal involvement in the future.

One of Harry's greatest areas of concern is the pollution of the our planet and its inhabitants, particularly with regard to energy pollution. This is something we do not see, but which is nevertheless very significant to our quality of life. Harry says:

'Fortunately, like all things in nature, both the gravity field of our planet and the energy field of our body appear to be designed to be perfectly balanced – not too strong and not too weak.

'The gravity field of the planet is affected by many terrestrial and extra-terrestrial factors, such as the moon, which influences the tides. But can you imagine what would happen to our planet if the gravity field were upset by an undesirable internal or external influence? For example, what would happen to the tides if the moon suddenly changed its orbit?

'Likewise, can you imagine what would happen to your body if your energy field were similarly disturbed? Well, unfortunately for all of us, undesirable internal and external influences upset the delicate balance of our energy field every single micro-second of every single day of our lives.

'The same goes for our physical bodies. Homoeostasis is the optimum balanced condition of the physical human body. But we get cold, we get hot, we eat things which don't agree with us, we smoke, we drink, we cut ourselves, we get viruses, we break bones ...

'All this puts our physical body out of balance and our energy field reacts in sympathy with this physical imbalance – and vice versa. I have confirmed this to my own satisfaction after more than 20 years of research, although it must be said that a number of others still need convincing.

'Allowing that both our energetic and physical selves are out of balance, I think it makes sense to do as much as we can to rebalance our energy as often as possible. This is the purpose of my EleCT machines.'

Harry expands on energy pollution:

'Many people are aware that we are increasingly being subjected to a thickening sea of radiation. It may be hard to convince ourselves that something we can't see, hear, touch, taste or smell can still affect us so detrimentally. Yet this fact must be faced in the future. But, in the same way that it has taken us a long time to learn a healthy fear of nuclear radiation, this is not always the quickest of processes. Certain scientists keep telling the public that we still do not know whether electropollution is a threat to human health. Some critics think this is a programme of deliberate disinformation – and they may have a point.

'Only time will tell whether this is true, but I for one am increasingly worried about the levels of electropollution.

These will not only grow in the future from the things we already know about, such as microwave ovens, computers and mobile phones, but also from things we may develop, such as electro-robots in the home.

'As satellites, gadgets for the person, car, home and office proliferate we will increasingly be bombarded by an invisible sea of radiation at rates of vibration which are not necessarily good for us. And you can't escape EM radiation – it's everywhere. Not the rosiest of scenarios, is it?'

These external energy fields are growing in number all the time, and their true effect on human beings is not yet known. In 1982, an editorial in the journal *Public Health* commented:

'Comparable alternating magnetic fields do not occur in nature. They only appear as a by-product of man's industrial activity, and comprise an influence for which there has been no opportunity for evolutionary adaptation.'

We referred earlier to Bernard Watson, Professor of Medical Electronics at St Bartholomew's Hospital Medical College. In 1987, after studying bioelectricity for decades, he wrote:

'[The study of pulsed magnetic fields] is a completely new area of biological interactions which are extremely difficult to research as they involve regulatory mechanisms and also field strengths so low that they have been previously considered to have no effect.

'Recently our study on the immunological changes brought about by exposing human lymphocytes to pulsed magnetic fields indicates that we should be aware of the dangers of environmental electromagnetic fields caused by 50 Hz power transmissions. We intend to pursue this work in order to establish the therapeutic use and also the dangers involved.'

As Harry says, 'The disturbing implication of Professor Watson's comments is that the sea of electromagnetism through which we are daily forced to swim may be having serious effects on our immune defences.'

If living in a sea of electromagnetism is reducing our ability to naturally fight disease, then Harry's electro-crystal generating machines – which restore balance to our energy fields – will become increasingly important as the electromagnetic mire thickens.

Roger Coghill and Harry were two of the first authors to put in print that some electromagnetic fields can be harmful. Roger Coghill was also on the TV news in December 1997 warning of the dangers of mobile phones and their effects. He was reported to be taking the unusual step of suing a mobile phone company on behalf of future victims of their equipment. Apparently, the waves used have a heating effect on any organisms they get close to.

'And we hold them next to our brains for minutes at a time!' says Harry with obvious concern. 'One answer is an earpiece and microphone on a wire connected to the main body of the phone which can then be held at a safe distance. But future developments such as disposable mobile telephones will only add to the electromagnetic assault on the brain and an increase in plastic refuse pollution.'

Given these potential hazards, perhaps Harry's machines, with their gentle and friendly vibrations, will be seen as invaluable rebalancers after a heavy day in the destabilizing electromagnetic atmosphere. Harry says: 'It is certainly true that more and more people are using the EleCT Method to wind down after a busy day. Increasingly many of us will need this sort of help to maintain our own natural vibrations.'

A question that is often asked is: 'How can some electromagnetism be harmful and some beneficial?' Harry believes that harmful effects from power lines, some domestic appliances and so on, tend to emanate from sources which are perhaps many thousands of times more powerful than his electro-crystal therapy machines.

Another point is the method by which Harry induces the electromagnetism into the human energy field. His 'tuning fork' of oscillating crystal chips creates a 'choir of voices' and the innate intelligence of the human energetic system decides which 'notes' it wants to accept. If Harry plays the wrong tune on his machine, the body just says, 'Don't like the sound of that' and rejects it, whereas an electricity pylon at the bottom of the garden is constantly booming out 'noise' at you which your body has no defence against.

Some scientists now believe that even our thought patterns can affect both our own energy field and that of others. Harry says:

'Thought is an invisible energy whose source is the mind/brain of an individual and whose effect we have very few means of measuring. But whether you think a good or a bad thought it reaches its destination immediately.

'I have developed instruments which appear to be able to measure the quantitive and qualitative effects of thought on the human energy field. Years of research results have convinced me that we affect everyone and everything around us perhaps as much by what we think as by what we say and do. All energy has a source and an effect.'

Another aspect of energy therapy which Harry is working on is electro-transplant therapy. He explained the rationale behind this:

'Think of the body like a choir. The individual members of the choir, the body's cells, want to sing in tune, and this they normally do by transmitting the correct signals to adjacent cells. If a few of the choir members start singing the wrong notes, then adjacent singers can remind them. In some cases the choirmaster, or brain, may need to intercede for harmony to prevail.

'However, in disease, too many of the choir start singing out of tune for the situation to be contained by the other choir members or its master. Outside help is required. I think that electro-transplant therapy can assist in this retuning process. We digitally record the melodious sound made by the healthy cells, and then play this back to those who have gone off-key to remind them of the correct notes needed for harmony to be re-established. Hopefully, once retuned, the choir can, with regular practice, maintain that balance.

'Where possible we try to take signals from the person themselves. If, for instance, someone has a problem with their left hand, we would take a signal from their right hand if that was transmitting a healthy signal.

'Where someone has a heart problem, we would have to take a signal from a healthy close relative who had no problems in that area. We have to be sure to take recording from a healthy site. We assess this by listening carefully to the medical history as told to us by the person. We also use ESM and PIP to discover if the site is relatively sound before recording a signal.

'Unfortunately I have not had the time or resources to develop this approach further, but I can tell you about a couple of cases where electro-transplant therapy has shown promise.

'A young man in his early thirties came to see me. He had a history of chronic kidney infections which had left him with poor renal function, so poor in fact, that the doctors were talking about putting him on renal dialysis.

'He came along, with his mother, to see if I would be able to help the situation. I told them about my research with electro-transplant therapy and they said they would be willing to try. I made digital recordings of the signals from his mother's kidney area, as her kidneys were functioning normally, and then played them back to his kidney region.

'This procedure was carried out for about an hour, once a week for a month. Renal function tests improved considerably after this and dialysis was put on the back burner.

The young man will come again in the future should there be any need for concern.

'Another case was that of an elderly gentleman who had angina pectoris [heart pain caused by insufficient blood supply to the heart muscle].

'Signals were recorded from his son's heart region, his son being a lot younger and healthier with no history of heart problems. The result was that the elderly gent had improvement in his symptoms. He was able to be more active as exercise tolerance increased, with substantial reduction in pain.'

Another successful case was reported by EleCT practitioner Guy Pilbeam, who said: 'For my own part I have a lump of fibrous tissue at the top of my pelvis from a fall 20 years ago. Electro-transplant therapy has definitely made it shrink and it is no longer so troublesome.'

Harry is hoping to do more research on electro-transplant therapy with colleagues in the Far East and Europe, but lack of resources has hampered him in this, as in other areas. When we asked him how he would like the research to progress he said, 'Well, for a start we need funds to purchase spectral analysis equipment.'

We once asked Harry if he had 'a really revolutionary large-scale idea'. He replied:

'For a long time now, I've been thinking about how we could digitally record all the good vibrations of schoolchildren when they are at their peak of physical fitness and energy balance in anticipation of things going wrong in the future.

'When they get older, most of them will experience ageing pains of one kind or another. They might in later life get, say, angina. We would have their vibrations stored on computer disk and we could simply open their "heart" file on the computer and play back their own healthy heart signals which were recorded all those years before.

'We can even record signals from a healthy child and play them back to an unhealthy parent, or transplant between well and sick siblings and so on. This isn't medical science fiction, it's called electro-transplant therapy and it could be implemented in schools on a nationwide basis tomorrow.

'And ... we could do it all by utilizing existing and widely available computer hardware and software, so the cost would be minimal when measured against the potential preventative and curative benefits.'

We asked Harry to expand on any other ideas he might have concerning the use of electro-transplant therapy in the future. He smiled as he created a vision of futuristic space medicine:

'Imagine a young space cadet is having his pre-space mission medical check-up. As well as taking readings of all his systems and energy flows, the computer is recording all the healthy signals from his various organs and tissues. This information will be stored on a miniature disk which he will carry with him for the next 25 years on his journey to Genesis Two, a small planet thought to have life-sustaining properties.

'The PIP space scanner (Version 35) has indicated, by the energy configurations surrounding this planet, that it is likely to have water, oxygen and an atmosphere conducive to humans. The 25-year mission will seek to confirm this potential new home for some of the 30 billion people who are beginning to crowd and suffocate the Earth.

'The young cadet's comfortable spacesuit is lined with tiny crystal chip oscillators and with this EleCT 200 system, he is able to regularly tune and balance his energy field for maintenance of optimum homoeostasis while in space.'

While this is obviously a fictional representation to illustrate the potential of Harry's work, crystals pre-programmed with the

Earth's vibration are already being used by astronauts to balance body energies.

Harry continued with his thoughts on this subject:

"Space research is moving on apace. The opening of a new space station is planned for 1998. Here scientists will be doing research into things like DNA proteins which cannot be done in the same way on Earth.

"Conventional medicine on a long space trip may be harder to practise. For example, a surgical operation would be very hard to perform since blood and other fluid containment would be difficult in zero gravity. Our EleCT machines might perform a preventative and curative function in space so that such invasive techniques would not become necessary.

'Lots of research is going on at the moment. In Russia, one volunteer spent a whole year in bed simulating weightlessness with his head below his feet. He experienced impaired function in all systems. Deployment of EleCT might have helped him rebalance quicker so that he could resume his normal activities sooner.'

The clockwork mechanism would also be an obvious advantage in space as it requires no energy input apart from a person's exertion. Perhaps this could also be used on submarine trips.

Harry has always been very interested in numbers and their relationship to life. In May 1987 the *Journal of Alternative and Complementary Medicine* reported on his work in an article entitled: 'Is God a genius with fractal equations?' Basing his research on the work of American mathematician Professor Benoit Mandelbrot, Harry had succeeded in converting a sequence of fractal equations – mathematical representations of natural forms – into what he regarded as 'life forms' using a basic home computer system.

Harry said at the time:

'We simply fed Mandelbrot's equations into the computer and are getting these astonishing life form patterns. They remind me of the living cellular shapes that so excited me when I first looked into a microscope – although an astronomer might equally feel that they remind him of a view of the cosmos through a telescope.

'What we've been able to do is formulate certain mathematical representations to the computer and this then produces a graphic picture on the computer screen. Sometimes by changing the formula you are not sure what the end result is going to be. Sometimes we've got what appear to be cells, sometimes we've got wonderful anatomical forms, sometimes plants, sometimes pictures of animals – just by changing the formula.'

Harry then showed us various computer print-outs of fractal pictures generated by his computer.

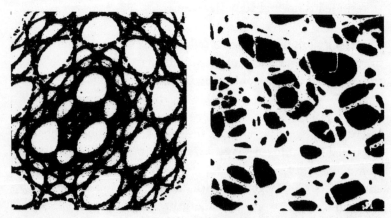

COMPARE THE COMPUTER-GENERATED FRACTAL IMAGE (LEFT) WITH THE MAGNIFIED HUMAN BONE SECTION (RIGHT).

'This is a starfish, achieved using a Newtonian cubed root. Newton had the mathematics for a starfish but didn't realize it. I'm not the only researcher in this area, but it's something that's fascinated me, and it's more than a hobby.

'Here I've got a mathematical formula generated graphic picture for bone, and here is a photo of real bone; the two appear to be very similar. Also, if we're dealing with these pure mathematics, we're talking here of pure energy and mathematical rules. If we can understand the mathematics, we can understand something of the projections of these rules into perhaps other forms.

'We've got a structure, say, of healthy bone. If we change a very small part of that formula we'll get a graphic that looks the same as osteoarthritis. This happens in nature, or the body does this through negative thinking, subconscious or otherwise, the build up of toxins, pollution and so on, which upsets the natural divine formula producing the said distorted result in the body.

'It's all about vibration. The physical molecules, the building blocks of life, are strung on these mathematical formulae which are really living dynamic energy patterns. What the computer does is make a static frozen wave form of them that we can look at and study.

'With the correct vibration we may be able to heal a bone for instance. I want to work on getting even more accurate results than we are doing at the moment.

'The extraordinary thing is the equations not only create shapes but once the shape is formed it seems to evolve of its own accord. How, we don't know and that is exactly what we are examining now. But we feel it may have something do to with the fact that carbon and silicon have the same electrical valency of four. We may in fact be looking at the secret of life in these patterns.

'I am beginning to believe that God, among his other very long list of talents, is basically a mathematical genius.'

Mathematics may have a place in the future of medicine, it seems. Harry continued:

'Our belief, based on our other work in electro-crystal therapy, is that living things are open harmonic systems influenced by other, external, harmonics.

'Harmonics can affect structure and the result could be disease. Crystals, for example, are simply standing wave forms if we accept, working backwards from $E = mc^2$, that all matter is congealed light. My belief is that there is a fundamental human harmonic which is then qualified by individual variations. Therefore, there must be a harmonic for each individual. If we can find that then we will be in the era of truly modern medicine in which we will use computers to diagnose and simple painless methods such as crystals, sound and lasers to heal. That is where I hope our work is taking us.'

As for agriculture, Harry's early work with Kirlian photography showed graphically the 'energy' fields of plants and he looked at how their growth could be promoted by boosting their energy field with electro-crystal therapy. This included the tomato plants he grew in a small greenhouse in his back garden:

'One year I decided to irrigate them with water that had been "energized" or "potentized" using D10, which is the highest frequency on the electro-crystal generator. This energized water, when drunk, has been known to improve the life-force of both humans and animals. We have even had cases of apparently dead fish which were floating on top of the pond. A few minutes of the crystal wand in the water on D10 and *voilà*, a resuscitated fish is swimming around again!

'Getting back to the tomato plants, I put the electrode, set on D10, into the water for about 20 minutes before sprinkling it on them.'

Normally Harry's tomatoes grew to between four-and-a-half feet and six feet. Those grown with D10 water grew to nine and ten feet tall! Although the plants were larger, the tomatoes were of average size. However, there were many more trusses and yield was significantly increased. An interesting feature was that the thistles which grew around the greenhouse got the friendly radiation 'fall-out' from the D10 water and grew to an enormous size of eight and even nine feet tall.

Harry thinks that this way of potentizing water could reduce disease in plants and help to avoid crop failures in the future. He explained:

'If you plant an acorn from a donor tree in Sherwood Forest and leave it well protected amongst similar oaks, it will grow to, say, 100 feet and live for 200–300 years or more.

'If you plant an acorn from the same tree on top of an open Welsh hill facing west, the growth and lifespan will be attenuated. Because it is an acorn from the same donor tree we can conclude that it is not the geno-type but the pheno-type (the environment) that has been altered.

'This is similarly true for a plant sprinkled with ordinary and D10 potentized water. With ordinary water it grows in one way, but by changing its environment – just through adding potentized water while all other conditions stay the same – we can make it grow bigger. In effect we have boosted the growth naturally by improving the environment, not by mucking about with the genes.

'Rather interestingly, my thistles also seemed to benefit from the D10 water treatment of the tomatoes. As I have said, in my view, this is a positive natural radiation effect. The implications for gardening and agriculture are obvious.'

There are now so many stories about the beneficial effects of electro-crystal therapy on plants that we have often wondered whether it would be worth a commercial agricultural company conducting a future study on its viability as a 'radio-fertilizer'.

Harry has also noticed that plants treated with electro-crystal therapy are free from aphids and other pests.

All sorts of mental and emotional imbalances have also responded to EleCT. This may be due to the multi-dimensional connections created by the chakras and energy bodies previously mentioned. Many have commented that they can foresee the potential for Harry's machines being used in the treatment of emotional disorders.

Some of these emotional imbalances could be the result of the electromagnetic waves produced by our technological age. Many of these are known to be disruptive to brainwaves. The use of crystals could help to re-establish normal brainwave patterns.

Specialized crystals are sometimes used to enhance this benefit. For example, some crystals, such as aquamarine, have been shown to have a calming effect, so a tube filled with this crystal only is used on people who need a very tranquillizing treatment.

It may be that a positive effect is produced more readily by combining orthodox treatment such as psychiatry with EleCT. Harry comments:

'The oscillating crystals seem to have a regulatory effect on the disharmonious brainwave patterns of the emotionally or mentally ill.

'Brain-related illness such as epilepsy and strokes have also responded well in many cases to EleCT.'

Some recoveries border on the miraculous. Harry says:

'It has been speculated that the "grounding" effect of crystals could be very useful in the treatment of epilepsy, because in an epileptic seizure the subtle bodies often become misaligned or completely separated form the physical body.

'Some hypnotherapists have reported that when they combine A3 [alpha rhythms] to the head or solar plexus in addition to their normal practice, emotional blockages seem to be more readily released.'

Kirlian photography is something Harry investigated some time ago. However, many modern researches are continuing this work and Kirlian technology may make a contribution to medicine in the future. For example we were invited to the headquarters of Body Shop during 1996 to demonstrate Harry's techniques. We found that this innovative and forward-thinking company, renowned for its concern for the environment, was already testing the ingredients for its products using Kirlian methods.

When we put Kirlian information on our web page on the Internet, we immediately started getting messages from doctors in places like Russia where the technique was first discovered and continues to be used for research.

This increasing interest in imaging the energies around people, plants, animals and other objects bodes well for PIP technology in the future. Harry says:

'One day we may see shoppers in the supermarket with their mini-PIP scanners looking to see what the subtle energy of the food they are choosing is like. There are many potential applications in industry, too, such as looking for stresses on aircraft.'

Another potential application may be in controlling the weather. Once when Harry went to Iceland, his colleagues there arranged for him to try a weather experiment at two airports, one at Reykjavik and another in the north of the country. The idea was to raise the barometric pressure near the airport to promote safer flying.

The weather bureau had agreed to oversee the results, but Harry was given to understand that the officials thought the notion of beaming electromagnetic energy into the atmosphere from a high point (top of a church in Reykjavik, top of a mountain in the north) via a huge crystal-filled tube to be a little whacky to say the least.

The idea was one that Harry had after a particularly troubled flight and bumpy landing in terrible weather conditions. 'I thought it must be possible to affect the weather at airports so that takeoffs and especially landings were a little less turbulent.'

Flying is not Harry's favourite activity at the best of times, so there was a little more than pure altruistic interest in this project.

In Iceland, customs, by now familiar with the eccentric crystal man from England, waved through the four-foot long tube of crystals in saline solution, otherwise known as Big Bertha (see plate section), without a second glance.

'We set up a very powerful electromagnetic generator near the airports,' Harry explained, 'and pulsed the energy through Big Bertha into the atmosphere.'

The people from the weather bureau were amazed to find that the barometric pressure did seem to rise in line with Harry's predictions. They did, however, suggest that it was not a project that they wanted to be involved in and there the idea died a very quick death. The reasons for the lack of official interest are uncertain, but Harry feels there are ways in which an ability to affect the weather could be important in the future:

'Normally nature can decide what is best. My idea would not be to change nature but to rebalance the effects of what we humans are doing to the planet. This is the whole thrust of my work, to help nature defend herself against the threat posed by humanity. Really, though, if you think about it, by attacking the planet we are attacking ourselves, because we are a part of the planet.

'In my view, the electromagnetic pollution we are causing with our microwaves, radar, mobile phones, televisions and so on is affecting the weather as much as it is affecting our bodies. But just as we can use electromagnetic energy to rebalance the human energy field after it has been polluted by harmful electromagnetism, so we can use it to rebalance the weather. Big Bertha has a whole family who could be placed strategically around the world to perform such a task.'

Could one reason why government officials are so wary of developing the ability to change the weather be that weather warfare is a real possibility in the future?

Certainly Harry believes that the future of medicine will be energy based, whether through ordinary energies such as electrical, electronic or electromagnetic, or extraordinary energies such as the subtle forces of ch'i and prana, chakras and meridians. The natural progression seems to be towards an increasing acceptance that energy medicine works, but there is still a great gap in our knowledge as to why and how it works.

Perhaps Harry Oldfield will continue to feature heavily in this progression to the more widespread use of energy medicine over the more physical biochemical techniques of the last two centuries. Perhaps the EleCT Method will spread around the world during the early part of the twenty-first century. Will each home have its own portable EleCT unit? When we have a headache, will we continue to reach for a chemical compound in the form of a pill or will we grab our 'magic machine' as Harry's generators have been dubbed?

We do not have crystal balls so we do not know the answers. But there are already therapists in 20 countries of the world. And thousands of magic machines have been bought. We can only wait and see.

REFLECTIONS

BY HARRY OLDFIELD

'The basic texture of research consists of dreams into which the threads of reasoning, measurement, and calculation are woven.'

ALBERT SZENT-GYORGYI

IN my private moments, I pray for guidance. Then I dream about all sorts of things. When I wake up, the answer is often there, crystal-clear, where yesterday there was only confusion.

There is an idea that human knowledge can be seen to progress in the same way as the quantum leap in sub-atomic physics: the electrons will only leap from one shell to another when the right amount or quantum of energy is present. Like climbing steps on a ladder, if you can only manage to raise your foot halfway to the next rung you tread air and the effort seems fruitless. Perhaps only when there is a sufficient body of knowledge – and (hard to measure) agreement between souls – will we be able to progress up the next rung, to make the quantum leap to the next shell, as it were.

And all progress appears to be fraught with problems. One of these is understanding what you are looking at and how to recognize a pattern in order to correctly interpret a situation. It was Alan Mackay who so wittily summed up the problems we encounter when we are looking for patterns and symmetries: 'Like the ski resort full of girls hunting for husbands and husbands hunting for girls, the situation is not as symmetrical as it might seem.'

On the subject of the patterns of life for which I have been searching for so long, modern physicist Gary Zukov says:

> Photons do not exist by themselves. All that exists by itself is an unbroken wholeness that presents itself to us as webs [more patterns] of relations. Individual entities are idealizations which are correlations made by us ... The new physics sound very much like the old Eastern mysticism.

It is these patterns of life which many people have tried to identify and understand in their search for the meaning of life. I have long thought that it is the invisible universe that may hold the clues to a greater understanding of 'being'.

In addition the visible universe suggests that in the part we may be seeing a glimpse of the whole. To understand the patterns in both is to perhaps be on the right path. William Blake wrote:

> *To see a world in a grain of sand*
> *Or heaven in a wild flower*
> *Is to hold infinity in the palm of your hand*
> *And eternity in an hour.*

Like Blake, I find it hard not to share the fascination I have for the patterns in which nature appears to be 'organized' by what I believe to be a Divine Being called God. So let us explore together...

What are the principles on which nature bases her structure and orders herself in ever more complex and exciting ways? In order to find out, join me on an imaginary journey. With our minds we can shrink to an infinitesimally small size in order to explore the micro-universe of atoms and molecules or expand ourselves to experience the macro-universe. We can speed to far distant galaxies. We travel from the present over the time horizons into the past and future time lanes.

The difficulty we generally have with truly understanding our environment is our own physical and sensory limitation and the added limitations of space and time, or space-time as we now understand it. But, in our mind, we have the vehicle with which we can be truly universal explorers. So, if you are ready, let us embark on our journey into the unknown.

Let us first look at what is considered the most simple building block of all matter: the atom. Or is it? Imagine for a moment that we are viewing a natural woodland scene. We are looking up at a magnificent oak tree with its giant trunk and twisting branches and what seem to be never-ending divisions of twigs and leaves.

We imagine ourselves small enough to be travelling through the sap-carrying vascular bundles inside the living wood. We go with the flow of the life-giving sap and eventually reach the end of a small twig. We steer a course into another branching system of leaf veins and shrink even further in order to follow the sap around box-like and circular structures called cells. These were once thought to be the building blocks of life as we know it.

However, realizing that there is still unexplored territory ahead, we are not satisfied with this level of understanding. By the power of our intention we become small enough to enter the nucleus of the cell. Around us we see huge fibrous bundles, tightly packed like rope. This 'rope', or DNA, contains all the information required to make another oak tree. (Many a scientist in the past would have given all his worldly goods for the secrets of this old rope.)

But we don't stop here. We shrink again until we can see the individual strands of DNA and then the molecular structure of the nitrogenous bases. We are awestruck. At this level we find it more difficult to see 'things' because all these molecules have become a vibrating and shimmering mirage. We pause to consider that no 'thing' can ever truly be 'still'. We now prepare to zoom in for the last time (on this trip) and focus on one group of molecular clusters.

Shrinking again, we now find ourselves in the atomic realm of the non-solid. Nothing is a solid thing at this level of reality.

Everything we see is made up of vibrating patterns of energy. These beautiful patterns seem to be formed by tiny vortices which twirl and pulse with concentric rings in ripples of energy. Looking at the vortices again, we see that where one wave front meets another, 'interference' patterns are set up which spread out to create further eddies and ripples and even more patterns. This whole process has produced the illusion of 'solid','still' matter which we will see when we return to our human 'macro-level' of the universe.

So we have discovered that there is nothing solid in the universe. What we perceive as solid is, in reality, energy of unusual wavelengths which creates visible patterns. Quantum physics and mathematical theories have supported this idea for quite some time.

When one of the greatest scientists of our age was asked to give his definition of matter, he said that the best way to understand it was as 'congealed light'. His name was Albert Einstein. Perhaps the mark of a genius is not one who can explain the most complex in the most complex way, but one who can explain the most complex in the simplest way.

We can go even further and say that light in its most stable state resembles what we perceive as solid matter but as it vibrates at higher and higher frequencies it becomes what we would normally understand as light once again. All of the electromagnetic spectrum, known and unknown, would be included in this description.

Before we were looking at an oak tree, which is a very complex living structure and might be described as non-typical of universal matter. A tree is not a stable example of matter – it has a constant molecular exchange with its environment with its need for CO_2 and water intake and so on. To see a very stable example of matter we need to imagine ourselves looking down at the Earth. To go below, we must first travel through the thin organic topsoil, a living, breathing part of the Earth, then through the mineral-rich deposits of the subsoil and still down further unto we hit bedrock. Don't panic – the pure energy of the mind knows no barriers save those it imposes on itself. With the power of our mind, we travel through solid rock as if it were melted butter.

Suddenly, something glistens ahead. We home in to discover a crystal. We admire its external symmetry and regularity of shape, which provide a startling contrast to the seeming disorder of jumbled rock around us.

The most stable state of matter that exists is the crystalline form. When you look at a crystal you are really looking at a giant lattice and the external appearance has a direct relationship to the orderly internal geometric arrangement. Any crystal represents matter in its most stable state, but this stability is on a knife-edge balance. Any introduction of energy, whether internal or external, can disturb this delicate balance and produce a registerable effect. This is one reason why crystals are so effective in energy manipulation.

Let us now take our minds back in time to those school geometry lessons and the sound of squeaky chalk on blackboard. Pythagoras' theorems take us off at various tangents and we learn perfect shapes and numbers. However, how many triangular trees and perfect straight lines have you seen in the natural world?

Mankind uses such artificial formula in his everyday environment to fashion his buildings and even his furniture and clothing. Nature, however, appears to use what we might call 'universal geometry'. Evidence of this is everywhere. To quote a wonderful mathematician and scientist by the name of Professor Benoit Mandelbrot, 'Clouds are not circles and mountains are not triangles!' A fellow of the IBM research institute in the USA and the father of fractal geometry, Mandelbrot coined the word 'fractal' to describe what mathematicians call 'monsters'. These 'monstrous curves' are so-called 'strange plots of fancy' which most mathematicians preferred to ignore because they did not conform to man-made constructs. Mandelbrot formulated a theory based on observation of nature, noting that she uses very different systems from the regular models created by man: the irregular, the jagged and the fragmented. Add this to the twisting and branching system of the trees and you have the universal geometry – straight from the mind of God.

Think for a moment of the most infinite detail contained in a finite area. This is the nearest that a non-mathematical mind might get to understanding a fractal. If we were to travel with our minds again to a mountain range and look at a single mountain from a distance we would observe a characteristic shape and form that enables us to identify it as a mountain. If we now zoom in on the top peak we will see that this section resembles the whole mountain. If we zoom even further in to the peak we will see even more detail, once again with a similar resemblance to the whole mountain. Now, if we pick up a stone on the peak, we will still see similarities to the giant whole.

Another analogy is given by Mandelbrot himself. This is the example of the apparent length of the coastline of an island like Britain. This would appear to be an easy observation at first sight. We would have to measure the length in miles. But on second thought we note that where we are observing from makes a difference to the result. If we use the view from a satellite in outer space and look at the Earth from a distance, we would observe an area of matter enclosed in an apparently definite and finite line, the coast. However, we soon realize that this is only an approximation and decide to zoom in closer. We see that the coastline gets more and more jagged as we see more detail and all this zigzag detail adds to the length of the line. Every nook and cranny, cove and niche must be measured. Now we go down even further and measure every crease and angle of rock, even down to the molecular level.

The length of the coastline seems to be increasing in leaps and bounds depending on our perspective. We soon come to accept that perhaps this frontier might be of infinite length as far as any reliably accurate measurement is concerned. We realize that somehow we have discovered that a finite area of land might be confined within a border of infinite length.

Having looked at the surface of the Earth, now let us turn our attention to the surface of our skin. Why? Well, here we have an apparently smooth surface of little complexity and the younger you are the smoother the surface (in theory). Let us zoom onto the surface of our own skin and see if we can find anything of interest.

The first thing we observe is that the surface is not smooth; this is the case however young or old we are. We observe huge boulders on a scaly convoluted surface with ripples and invaginations. The huge stone-like objects are minute dirt particles present even on the cleanest of skin. The scales are the remnants of dried up skin cells that at one time existed much deeper down in the dermis layer of the skin. There is nothing smooth here. Everything is jagged and rippled with contours of texture.

As we go down deeper we see plastic-like and more watery cells. The substance that surrounds them is lymphatic fluid. This provides the cells with protection and nutrition. Near these we see red doughnut-shaped cells swishing along at terrific speed in relation to the scale of things at this level. These cells are delivering oxygen and taking away carbon dioxide. We can also see amoeba-like cells. These creep around between the spaces looking for bacteria or particles of old cell detritus to absorb. This is a very important defence mechanism in the dangerous microscopic world that we have entered.

Let us now single out just one cell and zoom onto its surface. The surface of the cell is rippled and pitted, which increases the surface area of the cell, making it more absorbent amongst many other things. As we know from past journeys, even if we go down yet again to the tiny molecular structure, we will find that there are no flat or smooth surfaces. From this we can conclude that everything in the natural world has a fractal origin.

The straight line and perfect circle of Euclid only exist in man-made systems of geometry. And we try to model and structure our world within these guidelines! These are not natural guidelines and their implementation in almost every area of our lives could perhaps explain some of our disharmony with nature. This disharmony does not just occur externally in our environment but internally also. It permeates all physical and mental levels.

When we as collective modern man build our cities, we remove as much of nature as possible. We start by removing woodland or forest. We level off a hill or even divert a river. We make an artificial flat surface on which we lay down artificial rock foundations called reinforced concrete upon which we construct artificial caves in the shape of rectangular cubed boxes called flats or houses. When we look at any city we are looking at something which was once in the mind of men. It was transferred to papers called blueprints (a breeding ground for Euclidites) and from here was passed on to town planners and building construction workers who obtain their raw materials from the butchered natural environment.

We no longer cover our bodies with natural skins or fibres. We spin threads from the by-products of our artificial plastic environment. This whole situation leads to sympathetic disharmony between our minds and bodies and the Earth and universe in which we live.

My life's work has been to find ways of restoring some of nature's harmony and balance for as many people as possible. I hope I have succeeded just a little and look forward to making my small contribution in the future.

Now, I would like to say something more about crystals. The Earth is, in a sense, made of crystals, a pattern repeated throughout the universe. They were here before us and they will be here after us. Nearly all matter is crystalline. Most crystals are not carbon based and none need water for life, so we tend to dismiss the idea that they could be 'alive' and treat them accordingly.

But do living beings have to be water-dependent soft, fleshy, furry, feathery, tissuey, scaly things which move about on the land or in the sky or under the sea? It is a good question. Why should a crystal necessarily be any less alive than a plant, insect, bird or animal? All are composed of the same atomic building blocks. It is only our subjective definition as observers which makes one 'living' and another 'non-living'.

Graham Cairns-Smith of the University of Glasgow has proposed that the carbon-based 'living' forms that we see now may not have been the primary source of life's complexity. His hypothesis is 'genetic takeover'. The basic idea is that inorganic, self-replicating crystals of clay were the template from which complex, organic molecules – such as RNA and DNA – formed. In other words, the crystals 'showed' the carbon how to do more complex things in the first place and then the carbon was so good at replicating itself that the evolutionary result was takeover by the carbon-based life-forms who left little or no trace of their crystalline origins. Other commentators on this possibility have said that this whole process of genetic takeover is similar in style to the takeover of the United Kingdom's car industry by the Japanese, or perhaps the future silicon takeover of our own carbon-based chemistry.

In the mid-1970s, the science journal *Nature* also reported on the discovery, by a Dr Müller, of evidence for the part that crystals might have played in sparking the carbon-based evolutionary process with which we are all now so familiar.

Whilst the idea that crystals could have contributed to the development of carbon-based life is difficult for many people to accept at face value, if we think about it for a moment, this is the way that all evolution works. Whether it is the gradual adaptation of humans to their changing environment or the gradual takeover of one country's motor car industry by another, the evolutionary 'genetic takeover' effect is one that is observed and experienced everywhere.

It is this process that allows us to envision change and the logical steps that change takes. Remember that change seems to be essential. Without it the pond of life would probably stagnate.

We should also perhaps note that ancient Eastern wisdom suggests a progression of consciousness from the rock being to the plant being to the animal (conscious) being to the human (self-conscious) being.

All this leads us on to that contentious subject, the crystal-dwelling photonic being. Given that we do not know how life started and we are not sure that have not excluded certain forms by our definition of it, I would ask everyone to keep an open mind to the possibility that these things might exist.

When I saw the first silicon-based life presence I was with Helen Knowles *(see p. 20)*. I had photographed crystals before and had definitely seen some interesting emanations from my Kirlian photography days, but when Helen and I saw this 'thing' coming out of the crystal, I couldn't really believe it and for some time afterwards I had to keep on looking at the video footage to make sure I really had seen it. I can understand how some people can doubt their own eyes unless they have photographic evidence backing it up.

Since that first time we have seen many more beings and their presence has now been verified by other researchers using my equipment, which makes me feel very confident that they are real and not imaginary. Hopefully one day we will be able to prove to the satisfaction of the majority that these things exist.

When I first started on what can only be described as 'an incredible voyage of discovery', I certainly did not imagine that the variety of phenomena I have encountered were 'out there'. However as my instruments became more and more refined I have been increasingly able to see and measure more and more of these unseen realms.

The idea that there are unseen dimensions of reality is not a new one. For example, in the traditions of the East we have many such notions. In Western folklore we have dragons and elves and so on. In literature, Shakespeare alluded to our subject with 'There are more things in heaven and earth, Horatio, than are dreamt of in your philosophy.' And finally, perhaps we can look to the one whom I consider to be the ultimate guide for a little confirmation that we are on the right path on our journey into the invisible universe.

Jesus Christ said:

In my father's house there are many mansions. If it was not so, I would not have told you.

APPENDIX

THERE follows a very brief introduction to some of the ideas behind the application of electro-crystal therapy with relevant tables.

THE CHAKRA SYSTEM

Specific to Electro-Crystal Therapy (EleCT)

Electro-crystal therapy defines seven zones of the body which generally correspond with the ancient Ayurvedic medicine principle of the chakra system *(see Chakraman, in plate section)*. There are thought to be seven major chakras or energy centres. A chakra is thought to be a spinning vortex of energy. It is a configuration within and of energy, as a whirlpool is to water.

Harry believes that the chakras are related to the endocrine glands. These glands regulate the body by sending chemical messengers called hormones to different parts of the body.

The idea is very simple: balance the chakra to balance the gland to balance the body. Each endocrine gland is physically situated near its associated energy centre.

The chakras spin at their own specific frequencies. The slowest spinning chakra is the base and the fastest is the crown.

The chakras draw in energy from the universal energy field, which is then distributed via the meridians (channels) of the energy body to the cells of the physical body.

In ancient natural medical theory, there are thought to be a number of energy bodies each related to a physical, mental, emotional or spiritual aspect of the whole self. These are often depicted as a series of concentric egg-shaped rings extending out from the body, but are thought to 'interpenetrate' it and each other, thus producing one highly complex field specific to each individual. No two fields are the same.

These energy bodies do not necessarily occupy space in this space-time continuum. They may be, in effect, outside the physical universe. We can make a comparison with dreams, which are real in the sense that we experience them but they are not 'here' as such.

The chakras are thought to be 'step-down transformers' which transform energy from one energy body to another, bearing in mind that the bodies may be in different realities and so vibrating on varying levels.

The first energy body is known in ancient terms as the etheric body. It is the densest of all the energy bodies and is closely related to the physical body. It is thought to extend about one inch beyond the surface of the skin. On Chakraman you may notice that this first energy body is depicted as a 'haze' or 'mist' of energy around the body. (To avoid confusion this is the only energy body we have included in the diagram.)

The first energy body is the matrix or web of energy on which the physical molecules are strung. A good way to imagine this matrix is to think of those computer-generated 'net men' that are used as a framework on which to build up a design. The same programme is used on cars. The designer constructs a computer-generated 'net' which is a series of points joined by lines. The designer can then elongate or squash the net and so pull the bumper here, push the roof there and so on with the aid of the computer programme. If you can imagine a similar network of energy points which are joined by energy lines within your body, then you are beginning to grasp the idea of the energy scaffolding which Harry believes could be the original template of our form.

In Harry's view, the physical molecules are strung on this net and kept in place by it. The brain keeps all the points and lines in the right place by a 'radio-type' action transmitting instructions which tells them where to be and what to do.

If this is true we are much more complicated and complex beings than the purely physical model implies.

If you find it hard to accept that the brain is a quantum mechanical device which keeps our physical bits in the right place by means of the energy matrix then you may find it even harder to accept Harry's idea that the brain may also be working on other dimensions of reality at the same time. However, if this hypothesis is correct, then our brains may be somehow organizing the communication between our physical, mental, emotional, spiritual and perhaps other energy bodies in a way which we can only marvel at.

THE PHYSICAL POSITION OF
THE CHAKRAS

The crown chakra can be situated on the top of the head in some individuals. In others, it can be found in the area of the vertex. It can be imagined as a cone shape whose narrow end seems to emerge almost vertically from the head. The cone or whirlpool of energy gets wider as it extends upwards from the top of the head, a bit like an upside-down wizard's hat.

The brow chakra can be imagined as a similar cone arrangement which extends from the front of the brow.

The throat chakra can be similarly imagined as a cone arrangement which extends from the front of the throat but is also 'mirrored' at the back.

The heart chakra is in the area of the breast bone at the front and between the shoulder blades at the back.

The solar plexus chakra is in the area of the solar plexus and has a corresponding position on the spine at the back.

The splenic chakra is in the area of the umbilicus (navel) and has a corresponding position on the spine at the back.

The base chakra can be imagined as a cone or vortex whose narrow end starts at the base of the spine and widens as it extends from the body between the legs. The epicentre or eye of the vortex is located around the coccyx and its orientation is towards the Earth.

Harry has found that, in the male, the epicentre relating to the base chakra is located more towards the front of the body, corresponding to the position of the prostate. In the female, it is configured more towards the back of the body, corresponding to the cervix.

He has also observed with his ESM and PIP scanning systems that the position of the chakras can vary slightly from individual to individual. For example, the heart chakra may be found a little to the left or right of the midline in some people.

In dis-ease states the chakra may be seen to deviate from its normal 'healthy' position, i.e. energy flows may be so disrupted that the chakra is unable to maintain its normal position. Sometimes the chakra is below the normal surface of the energy body, other times it is gushing away like a solar flare.

COLOURS ASSOCIATED WITH
THE CHAKRAS

Harry has spent many years observing and experimenting with crystals and the effect they have on the human energy field. He has also observed the chakras and colours on the PIP system.

He has found that green crystals are very effective in the solar plexus region and that crystals with a yellow ray are very effective in the heart chakra zone. Harry theorizes that this seeming 'reversal' of the classical colours could be due to the fact that modern man has to cope with a polluted environment and that green (balance) is needed in the area of the solar plexus and its associated organs of cleansing and elimination, for example the liver and kidneys.

Each chakra colour represents a band of many colours (frequencies) in which one colour predominates rather than being the only colour found there.

CHAKRAS AND CRYSTALS

The seven major chakras are thought to be assembly points for the entry of energy from the universal energy field (UEF) into the human energy field (HEF). Chakras are, Harry believes, influenced by crystals and gems, depending on their colour or 'ray'.

In electro-crystal therapy the effect of sound, light and other electromagnetic frequencies on chakras is increased when they are pulsed through crystals. Each chakra responds to a different frequency band and pulse repetition rate in ascending order from base to crown. Similarly, each chakra responds to crystals of different colours of the spectrum in ascending order from red (base) to white (crown), with the exception of the green/yellow reversal.

Harry says the idea of different frequency bands or rates of vibration can be explained by an analogy to oil. The base chakra is like crude oil, earthy, sludgy and slow in its vibratory movement. The next chakra band (the splenic) operates or flows best at a slightly higher vibration, perhaps like petrol, and so on up the seven bands until we reach the crown chakra which – due to its brain, mind and spiritual associations – needs to operate at a much higher level. Harry likens the crown chakra's relative vibration to that of high-octane fuel.

When we are scanning people with PIP, we can often see that the 'wrong' energy is in the 'wrong' place. Using the analogy above, we might see crude oil where there is supposed to be high-octane fuel. This we would try to rectify with electro-crystal therapy.

The aim of electro-crystal therapy is to balance or normalize the vibration of each of the chakras using 'pulsed high-frequency electromagnetic energy' which is induced via crystals in saline solution (electrolyte) into the chakra system through a 'tuning-fork' effect.

Electro-crystal therapy attempts to balance and regulate the chakras in order to improve the function of associated physical, mental, emotional and spiritual aspects of the whole person. It aims to help the whole body/mind/soul entity that constitutes a human being to heal itself.

It is believed that when a chakra is balanced by an energy treatment such as acupuncture, healing or reflexology, it affects the whole person, including their 'subtle energy' aspects such as emotional state.

Harry Oldfield's electro-crystal therapy and other techniques represent an attempt to use machines to induce similar effects to those achieved by natural healing practitioners.

THE SEVEN MAJOR CHAKRAS
AND THEIR ASSOCIATED CRYSTALS
AND GEMS

Specific to Electro-Crystal Therapy

Each of the chakras is associated with certain crystals or gems, depending on their colour or ray.

CHAKRA	COLOUR	ASSOCIATED CRYSTALS & GEMS	FUNCTION
crown	white	clear quartz, rutile quartz, white topaz, white sapphire	general
brow	violet	amethyst, violet sapphire, fluorite, tourmaline	tranquillizing
throat	blue	blue sapphire, lapis lazuli, sodalite, turquoise, blue jasper, blue quartz, blue topaz, aquamarine, blue lace agate, bluejohn (Derbyshire)	tranquillizing
heart	yellow	citrine quartz, golden topaz, golden calcite, apatite, yellow agate, yellow sapphire, yellow diamond, tiger eye	golden healing ray
solar	green	emerald, jade, nephrite (Wyoming jade), aventurine, chrysoprase, green lace moss agate, green quartz, green tourmaline, green jasper, peridot (volcanic rock), turquoise, green opal (Iceland)	balancing
splenic	orange	carnelian, Mexican fire opal, orange jasper, orange agate, orange quartz	stimulating

base	red	ruby, garnet (poor man's ruby), red spinel, red jasper, red agate	stimulating, especially for circulation

The following should be noted when considering the benefits of crystals and gems. Harry has found white diamonds to be completely neutral and therefore lacking in any therapeutic benefits. Coloured diamonds work according to their ray. Amber is sometimes described as an 'organic gem' but is really a resin. However, amber is very 'electrical' and therapeutic. Rose quartz, rhodochrosite and pink agate are pink rays (a dilution of the red ray with white) and can be used on all chakras – from base to crown – with many therapeutic benefits.

THE SEVEN MAJOR CHAKRAS AND THEIR ASSOCIATED ENDOCRINE GLANDS

Specific to Electro-Crystal Therapy

Each of the chakras influences the function of its associated endocrine gland. The endocrine glands produce hormones which travel in the bloodstream. Hormones are chemical messengers whose function is to influence the activity, growth and nutrition of organs and tissues in the body. They regulate and maintain balance in the internal physical systems of the body. The simple aim of electro-crystal therapy is to balance the chakra to balance the gland to balance the body.

CHAKRA	COLOUR	ASSOCIATED ENDOCRINE GLAND	FUNCTION OF GLAND
crown	white	pituitary	Master gland: regulates activity of most endocrine glands; influences growth, sex hormones, etc.
brow	violet	pineal	Influences diurnal (day and night) rhythms, sleep patterns.
throat	blue	thyroid	Regulates general rate of metabolism. Body metabolism can 'idle' too slowly or 'rev' too fast.
heart	yellow	thymus	Immune system: defends against infections. Underworking = low immunity to disease; overworking = body attacks itself in conditions like rheumatoid arthritis.
solar	green	adrenals	'Fight or flight' mechanism. Overworking = stress, hypertension (high blood pressure); underworking = tiredness, lethargy.
splenic	orange	pancreas	Regulates sugar metabolism. Sugar level in blood should be stable to provide constant energy for cells. Too much or too little can lead to problems including coma.
base	red	gonads	Ovaries and testes: regulate production of the sex hormones oestrogen and testosterone.

Minor Chakras and Acupuncture Points

There are said to be 21 minor chakras – for example the two in the palms of the hands through which healing energy is thought to flow – and hundreds, perhaps thousands, of even smaller chakras, perhaps the points used in acupuncture. The latter are tiny vortices (hundreds of mini-whirlpools) at which energy configures as it flows on its journey around the human body/mind/soul system.

Some people, like Dr Richard Gerber, think that the chakras are transformers which change the rate of vibration of the energy as it flows around the body so that it can best regulate, normalize and balance the particular region, gland or aspect it is associated with. We do know that a whirlpool-like vortex is nature's way of changing the pace of things. Spiral galaxies are just one example. Perhaps this energy transformation is regulated by some innately intelligent energetic system of which we have very little scientific knowledge to date.

Meridians: Rivers of Energy

It is thought that the energy travels from chakra to chakra, that is, from whirlpool to whirlpool, along rivers called meridians. These energy rivers, much like rivers of water, can flow as little streams or huge wide rivers.

Meridians are thought to be pathways of least electrical and other energetic resistance. We all know what happens if a river pathway becomes blocked at the gross material level – the water goes around, over or under the obstruction and carries on its merry way. In other words, the river does not stop flowing, it changes course. Even a dam cannot contain it for long.

Harry has certainly found that living animals and people have vibrant channels or rivers of this subtle energy whereas in dead things it 'disappears' or at least 'departs'. So what motivates this mysterious flow of energy? What is its source? Where does it go?

POSTSCRIPT

Harry Oldfield has been researching his innovative ideas for some 20 years.

Like many an innovator before him, for most of this time he has been on 'the fringe' of science. However, just as we are finishing this book, in May 1998, Harry has been offered two visiting professorships to teach holistic health and energy medicine, one in Europe and one in Asia.

One of his current research projects, PIP microscopy, is now attracting the attention of mainstream scientists. This method utilizes Harry's ideas about light interference patterns to reveal hitherto-unseen images of the microscopic universe in its living, vibrant energy state.

A major feature of this imaging technique is that bacteria, cells and other micro-organisms can be studied in a living, moving state; without the need for staining – and thus killing – the specimen.

Harry's work researching the energies that may be present in mortuaries is continuing. This, like many of his other areas of research, could be very important to changing our view of the world in which we live. And even to the way we understand life itself. We think this work is hugely important.

Only time will tell.

SEleCT

THE SCHOOL OF ELECTRO-CRYSTAL THERAPY

Offers training in:

Electro-Crystal Therapy (EleCT)

&

Polycontrast Interference Photography (PIP)

CEleCT

THE CLINIC OF ELECTRO-CRYSTAL THERAPY

Open for:

Electro-Scanning Method
Polycontrast Interference Photography
Electro-Crystal Therapy
Opto-Crystal Therapy
Electro-Transplant Therapy

For all enquiries, appointments and for details of a
therapist in your area/country please contact:

The School & Clinic of Electro-Crystal Therapy
117 Long Drive
South Ruislip
Middlesex
HA4 0HL

Telephone/Fax 0181-841 1716
Email: eileen.oldfield@which.net